D0976942

CUCKOO

BY THE SAME AUTHOR

Cuckoos, Cowbirds and Other Cheats

An Introduction to Behavioural Ecology

Dunnock Behaviour and Social Evolution

CUCKOO

Cheating by Nature

Nick Davies

With field drawings by James McCallum

BLOOMSBURY
NEW YORK • LONDON • NEW DELHI • SYDNEY

Bloomsbury USA
An imprint of Bloomsbury Publishing Plc

1385 Broadway
New York
NY 10018
USA

50 Bedford Square
London
WC1B 3DP
UK

www.bloomsbury.com

BLOOMSBURY and the Diana logo are trademarks of Bloomsbury Publishing Plc

First published in Great Britain 2015
First U.S. edition published 2015

Map p. 241 by John Gilkes

ISBN: HB: 978-1-62040-952-7
PB: 978-1-62040-954-1
ePub: 978-1-62040-953-4

Library of Congress Cataloging-in-Publication Data has been applied for.

2 4 6 8 10 9 7 5 3 1

Typeset by Hewer Text UK Ltd., Edinburgh
Printed and bound in the U.S.A. by Thomson-Shore Inc., Dexter, Michigan

For Tim Birkhead
now forty years of friendship

Contents

Male cuckoo calling, having just displaced another male from a favourite perch.
Wicken Fen, 21 June 2014.

Preface

Cuck-oo . . . Cuck-oo . . .

As common cuckoos arrive back in Britain from their African winter quarters, the male's far-carrying call is a welcome harbinger of spring. For centuries, this has been a sign that the cold, dark days of winter are coming to an end, raising our spirits in anticipation of the warmth of the sun returning and a season of new growth. The oldest song in English, which dates from around AD 1250, is the cuckoo song:

> Sumer is icumen in,
> Lhude sing cuccu,
> Groweth sed, and bloweth med,
> And springeth the wode nu,
> Sing cuccu!

For the oldest reference to the cuckoo in European literature, we have to go back over 2,500 years, to ancient Greece in *c.*700 BC, when Hesiod recommended that the best time for ploughing is as the cranes are arriving for winter (mid-November), but otherwise it's better to wait for signs of spring, when the first cuckoos are calling (March).

The name *common* cuckoo is apt: the breeding range of the species extends across two-fifths of the earth's land surface, including not only the whole of Europe (except for Iceland), but stretching east through Asia, across Siberia to Japan, and south to the Himalayas, China and southeast Asia. Cuckoos that breed in the west of this range winter south of the Sahara, in Africa, while those breeding in the east winter in southern Asia.

Every spring, then, we can imagine waves of cuckoos passing north, right across the temperate regions of the Old World. In many languages, it's the call that gives the bird its name, so the waves are of cuckoos announcing their own arrival. Across Europe, the first calling waves reach the Mediterranean in March:

> '*cuco*' in Spain and Portugal, '*cuculo*' in Italy, '*koúkos*' in Greece . . .

They continue, up through central Europe:

> '*coucou*' in France, '*kuckuck*' in Germany, '*koekoek*' in the Netherlands,
> '*kukulka*' in Poland, '*kakukk*' in Hungary . . .

And they reach northern Europe from mid-April to May:

> '*cuckoo*' in the UK, '*käki*' in Finland . . .

The waves pass north through Asia, too:

> '*guguk*' in Turkey, '*gugoo*' in Azerbaijan,
> '*kuku*' in Kashmir, '*pug-pug*' in Nepal, '*akku*' in Bhutan.

Over this vast region of forest and open country, humans may have been listening out for cuckoos to announce the spring ever since our ancestors walked out of Africa and into Eurasia many thousands of years ago.

In Britain, the call has always been greeted with special affection by the public, and until 1940 *The Times* newspaper published 'first cuckoo' letters every year. In the race to be first, this sometimes led to over-eager claims:

> From Mr Lydekker, FRS.
>
> *6 February 1913*. While gardening this afternoon I heard a faint note which led me to say to my under-gardener, who was working with me, 'Was that the cuckoo?' Almost immediately afterwards we both heard the full double note of a cuckoo, repeated either two or three times . . . There is not the slightest doubt that the song was that of a cuckoo.

Six days later, Mr Lydekker wrote again:

> *12 February 1913*. I regret to say that, in common with many other persons, I have been completely deceived in the matter of the supposed cuckoo of February 4. The note was uttered by a bricklayer's labourer at work in the neighbourhood of the spot whence the note appeared. I have interviewed the man, who tells me that he is able to draw cuckoos from considerable distances by the exactness of his imitation of their notes, which he produces without the aid of any instrument.

Nevertheless, not all early records are mistaken. One year another letter, also claiming a February record, provoked a sceptical reply from an eminent ornithologist. Two days later, this expert received a parcel by post containing the body of a cuckoo.

The regular seasonal rhythm of the cuckoo's activities is celebrated, too, in a charming poem for children written by Jane Taylor (1783–1824). It was set to music a century later by

Benjamin Britten and is still sung with enthusiasm in schools across the country:

> Cuckoo, cuckoo . . .
> What do you do?
> In April, I open my bill.
> In May, I sing night and day.
> In June, I change my tune.
> In July, far, far I fly . . .
> In August, away!
> I must.

However, behind all these glad tidings there is a darker side to the life of this messenger. For many species of birds the spring invasion by cuckoos is neither charming nor a cause for celebration. The poet Ted Hughes senses a forewarning in the male's call:

> That first ribald whoop, as a stolen kiss
> Sets the diary trembling.

But it is the less familiar and haunting cry of the female cuckoo that proclaims the deed is done. After laying each egg, she utters a series of chuckles as if in triumph, for the common cuckoo is Nature's most notorious cheat. It never raises its own offspring. Instead, it lays its eggs in the nests of other birds, just one egg in each host nest. Soon after the cuckoo chick hatches, it throws the host's eggs and young out of the nest. Every summer, millions of small birds will have their eggs and chicks tossed aside by young cuckoos. Once the cuckoo chick has claimed the nest to itself, the host parents are tricked into spending their summer raising a young cuckoo instead of their own offspring.

For me, as a naturalist and scientist, the call of the cuckoo is not only a harbinger of spring. It's an invitation to solve an enduring puzzle: how does the cuckoo get away with such outrageous behaviour?

I have been a bird watcher all my life. I was born in the village of Formby, some 15 kilometres north of Liverpool on the coast of northwest England. One of my earliest memories is of putting out food for the birds in the garden at home and the thrill of a close view of a male chaffinch from a makeshift hide of wooden chairs. I must have been about six at the time, and I had never seen anything so beautiful. I became hooked for ever. Every autumn, pink-footed geese would arrive from their Icelandic breeding grounds to winter on the farmland behind the village. Skeins flew over our house at dusk on their way to roost and, when they became disoriented on foggy nights, I lay in bed marvelling at their cries.

I have no idea where this early passion for natural history came from; my parents encouraged me, but neither they nor my siblings (two younger brothers and a younger sister) developed this obsession. By the age of nine I was keeping neat records of the species I had seen. My first notebook lists 137 bird species for the year and has an entry for 1 May: 'Cuckoo calling, first of the summer!' – the exclamation a mark of my excitement. Perhaps I was already imprinted on cuckoos and the wide skies of the open countryside back in those boyhood days.

During my teenage years I began to learn that there was more to natural history than simply making lists of what I'd seen. Two books in particular inspired me: *The Life of the Robin* by David Lack and *The Herring Gull's World* by Niko Tinbergen. Lack's study, done in the 1930s at Dartington in South Devon, involved catching robins and placing coloured rings on their legs so that individuals could be recognised and followed throughout their lives. Now I began to see the world through a bird's eye and to appreciate the problems it faced in defending a territory, finding food and mates, choosing a place to nest, caring for its young, avoiding predators and so on. I was introduced to a scientific approach, too, namely one of asking questions about why animals behave in a particular way.

Niko Tinbergen thrilled me with his experimental approach. For example, he showed that birds reacted to simple stimuli in their environment. An adult gull would incubate any egg placed in its nest, even one of a different colour and size from its own eggs, and a begging gull chick would peck even at a cardboard model of an adult's beak, in anticipation of a regurgitated meal. I began to dream of a life spent outside, watching and wondering about birds and the natural world.

Later, when I was a biology student at Cambridge University, I often cycled out to Wicken Fen, a patch of old fenland 15 kilometres northeast of the city. It was here that I saw my first cuckoo egg in a reed warbler nest, and then watched reed warblers hard at work feeding a cuckoo chick. Perhaps this experience finally sealed my fate, because when I returned to Cambridge in my late twenties, to teach and do research in animal behaviour and ecology, my thoughts turned to the cuckoo once more, and I began to wonder about how it tricks its hosts.

Surely, I thought, the hosts should throw out any cuckoo eggs that appeared in their nests. If hosts did that, perhaps cuckoos would then evolve an egg that was hard to detect, one that looked exactly like the host's own eggs. What would the hosts do then? Would they be doomed to always accept the cuckoo's egg, or could they evolve other defences? It began to dawn on me that this would be a wonderful opportunity to study cheating in nature, with the potential to discover a natural 'arms race' in which host defences and cuckoo trickery might evolve together, side by side.

Together with my colleagues, I have been studying this evolutionary battle between cuckoos and hosts for the past 30 years. The aim of this book is to take the reader on a journey, to discover how evolution has designed host defence and cuckoo trickery. My hope is that this reads like a nature detective story, as we uncover how the cuckoo has tricks to slip past host defences, to lay its egg and to entice the hosts to feed its chick. Just as a detective has to examine details to solve a crime, so the naturalist has to look closely too – at adult cuckoo behaviour, at cuckoo egg colour and markings, and at cuckoo chick begging calls – to work out exactly how cuckoos trick their hosts.

Sometimes we will follow the cuckoo's trail simply by watching carefully. But cuckoos are secretive, so we will also need the tools of forensic science, such as DNA profiles and satellite tracking. We will make some shocking discoveries as we learn of the ingenious and often ruthless methods that cuckoos employ to trick and manipulate their hosts. This trickery is not confined to adult cuckoos; some of the most surprising tricks are those that cuckoo chicks use to persuade their foster parents to feed them.

However, I want not only to discover *how* cuckoos behave, I want to explain *why* they behave the way they do. This will entail asking questions about why various tricks are successful in deceiving hosts. For this part of our investigation we need to follow our watching by wondering, to form hypotheses. We will then follow Tinbergen's lead and test our ideas, our hunches, by field experiments. For example, with the aid of model eggs painted various colours, we will investigate why hosts are tricked into accepting a cuckoo egg as one of their own. Experiments with stuffed cuckoo mounts will help us to discover why the female cuckoo has to be so quick when she visits a host nest to lay her egg. Broadcasts of chick calls at a nest will reveal why the begging calls of cuckoo nestlings are so effective at manipulating their foster parents. The results of these experiments will often produce surprises, sometimes revealing that our favourite hypotheses are wrong and sending us off down new paths of discovery.

Wicken Fen has been my outdoor laboratory for the past 30 years. It might seem obsessive to have studied cuckoos for so long in one place. But each spring I'm as excited as ever by the first cuckoo call of the year, and because a human brain can never hold all the wonderful sights and sounds of the natural world, every summer comes as a fresh surprise. I love the fen in all its moods: the ever-present sound of reeds whispering in the breeze; the succession of flowers through the season, from the pale pinks of lady's smock that bloom when the first cuckoos arrive in April, to the yellow irises and red marsh orchids in May and June, when cuckoos lay their eggs, to the purple marsh thistles and creamy meadowsweet in July, as adult cuckoos depart for Africa once more. I have tried to convey the excitement of being a curious naturalist in the field, so the atmosphere of the fens looms large. Each year has brought new discoveries and these, in turn, raise new questions, so the science is refreshed too, and the journey is never-ending.

However, our detective work will take us way beyond the Fen, to study common cuckoos and their hosts not only throughout the UK, but across Europe to Japan. We will discover that evolutionary change is relentless. In some places, cuckoos are encountering new host species, which are only just beginning to evolve defences. We will also find isolated populations of hosts that are no longer parasitised and are slowly losing their defences. These are thrilling examples of evolution in action, a corner of Darwin's 'entangled bank', where animals and plants are continuously evolving to keep up with the changes in their enemies and competitors. We also travel out to Africa and Australia, in search of other cuckoo species which have been doing battle with their hosts for far longer, and where cuckoo trickery and host defences are even more intricate. Nature is always a source of surprise and wonder.

The story is a human one, too, of our changing perceptions of the natural world – from the bewilderment of those from past centuries who struggled to understand why a Creator would produce a creature that lacked any affection for its offspring, to observers now who are fascinated by the outcomes of evolution. We will pay homage to early naturalists whose discoveries laid the foundation for cuckoo studies today. They include: Aristotle, who, over 2,300 years ago, already knew that cuckoos laid their eggs in other birds' nests; William Turner from the sixteenth century, who wrote the first book about birds in Britain; John Ray from the seventeenth century and Gilbert White from the eighteenth century, both puzzled by the cuckoo's parasitic habits; White's contemporary Edward Jenner, whose first detailed descriptions of a cuckoo chick evicting host eggs and chicks from the nest were so astonishing that they were widely disbelieved; Charles Darwin, Alfred Russel Wallace and Henry Walter Bates, evolutionary thinkers and brilliant field naturalists from the nineteenth century; Alfred Newton, from the late nineteenth century, who wrote about the various races of common cuckoos, each specialising on a particular host species; Edgar Chance, a passionate egg collector from the early twentieth century, who was the first to discover how the cuckoo lays her egg; and Charles Swynnerton, another naturalist from the early twentieth century, who pioneered studies of cuckoos and their eggs in Africa.

These are all heroes, but I feel a special bond with two of them. In 1530, William Turner was elected a Fellow of Pembroke

College in Cambridge, the college where I was a student and where I've been a Fellow, too, since 1979. His book on birds, published in 1544, has a 'Peroration to the reader' that heralds a change in our view of the natural world, from the unquestioning acceptance of folklore to fresh scientific enquiry:

> This little book of mine contains within it many more conjectures than sure statements . . . it seemed to me much more prudent and becoming on a subject that is difficult and not yet sufficiently explored to tread doubtingly and modestly by conjecture, and so to enquire, than to pronounce rashly and immodestly on things undetermined.

My concerns about cuckoos are very different from those of Turner, nearly 500 years ago, but I hope his spirit of asking questions of nature and admitting when we don't know all the answers lives on in my book, too.

The other person peering over my shoulder as I wrote is Alfred Newton, Professor of Comparative Anatomy at the University of Cambridge. When he died in 1907, he bequeathed his grand old desk to the Zoology Department, where I have studied and taught for most of my life. I am privileged to have this in my room, and so have written my book at the very same desk on which Newton wrote about cuckoos, over 100 years ago.

Today, there are no more 'first cuckoo' letters to *The Times*. If there were, they would probably be letters remarking on the silence, wondering where all the cuckoos have gone to, for there has been an alarming decline in the last 50 years or so. I hope, by the end of our journey, that the reader will agree with me that their disappearance would be doubly sad: we would lose not only our harbinger of spring, but also some of the most amazing dramas of natural history anywhere on earth.

1

A cuckoo in the nest

Reed warbler feeding a cuckoo nestling, 11 days old, with a bill-full of flies. Reach Lode, 25 May 2014.

Is there anything more extraordinary in the natural world?

Early morning, a still summer's day in mid-July, not a breath of wind; I'm searching along the edge of a reed-fringed ditch on Wicken Fen, a patch of ancient fenland just north of Cambridge, and Britain's oldest nature reserve. This is a vast, flat landscape; big skies encircle me to the horizon and reflect in the water below, so sometimes I feel I am floating through the sky itself. The white sails of an old wind pump shine brightly in the sunshine. A marsh harrier appears over the reed tops and drifts close by on upswept wings, a young moorhen in its talons. On the path, there are fresh molehills of black peaty soil, the matted remains of old fen vegetation. The peat is resting on a bed of water and, as I walk along, the ground sways gently below my feet.

Just ahead, in the middle of the ditch, a reed twitches. From that exact spot I hear a loud, high-pitched and persistent, quivering call: '*tsi . . . tsi . . . tsi . . . tsi . . .*' I approach slowly and with a long hazel stick, I gently part the reeds. The calling ceases. In the silence, I hear the dew that I have dislodged from the leaves dropping into the water below. Hidden in the darkness, halfway up the reeds, is a reed warbler's nest. It's a neat cup, woven from thin strips of old reed and suspended from three vertical stems about a metre above the water surface. Sprawled on top, with its wings draped over the nest rim on either side, is an enormous common cuckoo chick. It is two weeks old, fully feathered, and it sits perfectly still, with its bill shut tight, but it is watching me intently through brown beady eyes.

I lean out from the bank to get a better look; as I do so, the cuckoo suddenly rears up, its head feathers erect, and it opens its beak wide to reveal its gape, a blaze of bright orange. Then it makes a lunge towards me. Instinctively, I withdraw my hand as if expecting an attack. My heart is beating fast, but then I find I'm smiling in admiration at the cuckoo's show of bravery. We look at each other for a moment; then I withdraw my stick and the reeds spring back, but not completely. Now there is a little gap through which I can watch the cuckoo from the bank just five metres away. I sit quietly and focus on it with my binoculars.

After a few minutes, the reeds twitch once again and a reed warbler emerges from the forest of reed stems, clinging to a reed just above the nest. It has a bright blue damselfly in its bill. The warbler gazes down and appears tiny next to the monstrous cuckoo chick below, some five times the warbler's own weight. The cuckoo immediately begins a frenzy of calling, vibrating its open gape. Without a moment's hesitation, the warbler bows deep into the enormous mouth to deliver the food. As it does so, the reed warbler's head is almost completely engulfed. For a brief moment its small eye lies buried at the base of the gape, right next to the cuckoo's large eye, and the warbler seems to risk being devoured itself. But the warbler withdraws just before the large gape clamps shut on the prey, leaving the tip of the damselfly's abdomen sticking out. Another twitch of the reeds, and the warbler slips off to search for another meal.

I am amazed by what I have just seen. Reed warblers have many wonderful adaptations for their insectivorous life in the reeds. They navigate by the stars from their winter quarters in sub-Saharan Africa to breeding grounds in Europe. They must have an excellent memory for local landmarks, too, because adults that I have colour-ringed, so they can be recognised individually, return to exactly the same territory each summer. The females select their mates carefully, based on territory quality and song repertoire. Females then build exquisite nests, anchored to the supporting stems with woven strips of reed and spider silk, just the right size to keep a brood of four reed warbler young snug and warm, and deep enough to keep them safe as the reeds sway in the wind. The pair then select choice prey items for their young, rejecting prey that are unprofitably small (tiny midges) or too large to handle (large dragonflies). So the warblers are admirably careful in their choice of where to live, who to mate with and what to eat. Why, then, when confronted by a young cuckoo, so different in appearance and far too big to be one of their own chicks, are they apparently so stupid?

I am amazed by the cuckoo chick, too. How does this enormous chick stimulate the little warblers to bring enough food? It's now mid-July and all the adult cuckoos left the fen two weeks ago. Some may already be in their African winter quarters while their last chicks are still being tended by reed warblers back in Britain. Why do cuckoos abandon their young and entrust them to another species?

I am not the first to experience this astonishment, of course. These marvellous interactions between common cuckoos and their hosts have fascinated human observers since ancient times. It has long been known that the cuckoo lays its eggs in the nests of other species. Over 2,300 years ago, Aristotle (who lived from 384 to 322 BC) recorded that 'it lays its eggs in the nest of smaller birds after devouring these birds' eggs'. He knew that the cuckoo then relied entirely on the host species to raise the young cuckoo:

'they do not sit, nor hatch, nor bring up their young.' And he also knew that the newly hatched cuckoo chick ejected the host eggs and young and so became the sole occupant of the nest: 'when the young bird is born it casts out of the nest those with whom it has so far lived.'

In 1248, the Holy Roman Emperor, Frederick II, a keen falconer and fascinated by bird behaviour, also described the cuckoo's parasitic habits:

> The bird called cuckoo makes no nest nor lays eggs on the plain ground, nor feeds young, but obligately lays its eggs into foreign nests, for instance those of blackbird or praeni [a meadow-nesting songbird] or other birds, which incubate its egg and rear its young. Once I got a nest of praeni with an untypical nestling having a large gape. After having reared this nestling with thorough care by my helper we realised that this is a young cuckoo. Therefore, we know clearly that the cuckoo does not build its own nest, but lays its eggs into the nests of foreign birds.

There are also frequent references in old literature to the cuckoo's odd behaviour. This bird riddle, translated from Old English, is in *The Exeter Book*, a manuscript dating from AD 950–1000, and surely refers to a cuckoo egg and then the cuckoo chick being cared for by foster parents:

> In these days my father and mother gave me up as dead; nor was there a spirit for me as yet, a life within. Then a certain very faithful kinswoman began to cover me with garments, kept me and protected me, wrapped me in a sheltering robe as honourably as her own children, until I, under the garment, as my fate was, grew up, an unrelated

stranger. The gracious kinswoman fed me afterwards until
I became adult, could set out further on my travels.

The young cuckoo's vigorous begging in the host nest must also have been familiar. In Chaucer's poem from *c.*1382, *The Parlement of Foules*, the young cuckoo is chastised as a symbol of greed (line 612):

Thow rewtheless glotoun!

And the adult cuckoo's lack of parental care often comes to symbolise a life with no love at all. In another fourteenth-century poem, *The Cuckoo and the Nightingale* by Sir John Clanvowe, an opposition is set up between these two birds. The nightingale argues that love is the mainspring of

al goodnesse, al honour and al gentilnesse . . . perfyt joy.

The cuckoo replies that the nightingale's complicated song, with its embellished phrasing, is obscure, while his own simple call, 'cuck-oo', 'trewe and pleyn', is easily understood by everyone. His message is that 'lovyng is an office of dispaire', that will bring nothing but pride, sorrow, envy, distrust, jealousy and eventual madness.

These two birds continue their dispute in a German folk poem from the early nineteenth century, set as one of the songs in Gustav Mahler's 1892 song cycle *Des Knaben Wunderhorn* (The boy's magic horn). Here, the argument is over which is the finer singer. The cuckoo's cunning nature is revealed when he suggests they ask the donkey to act as judge, 'for he has two big ears, all the better to tell which is best'. The nightingale goes first, but its song is too intricate for the poor donkey. When it's the cuckoo's turn, the donkey immediately appreciates the simple call and, with a cry of 'ey-aw', pronounces the cuckoo the winner of the contest.

The cuckoo is also associated with betrayal, a 'cuckoo in the nest' becoming a symbol of an illegitimate child, the violation of a man's own domestic nest. In *Love's Labour's Lost*, written in the 1590s, Shakespeare makes a play on the words cuckoo and cuckold, a man whose wife has been unfaithful and so who might be raising another man's child as his own:

> When daisies pied and violets blue
> And lady-smocks, all silver white,
> And cuckoo-buds of yellow hue
> Do paint the meadows with delight,
> The cuckoo then on every tree
> Mocks married men, for thus sings he
> Cuckoo!

Thus the call of the cuckoo comes to instil a fear of cuckoldry. Milton's 'Sonnet to the Nightingale', from about 1629, when he was a student at Cambridge, refers to the superstition that hearing the cuckoo in spring before the nightingale foretells bad luck for a lover:

> O Nightingale, that on yon bloomy spray
> Warblest at eve, when all the woods are still,
> Thou with fresh hope the lover's heart dost fill,
> While the jolly hours lead on propitious May;
> Thy liquid notes that close the eye of day,
> First heard before the shallow cuckoo's bill,
> Portend success in love; O if Jove's will
> Have linked that amorous power to thy soft lay,

Now timely sing, ere the rude bird of hate
Foretell my hopeless doom in some grove nigh;
As thou from year to year hast sung too late
For my relief, yet hadst no reason why.
Whether the Muse, or Love call thee his mate,
Both them I serve, and of their train am I.

How did early observers explain the cuckoo's strange behaviour? We are so familiar with our own strong parental feelings, and with sights of animal parents working hard to feed and defend their young, that the cuckoo's habit of abandoning its offspring seems both cruel and unnatural. The seventeenth-century naturalist John Ray regarded the beautiful fit between an animal's design and its mode of life as evidence for the wisdom of God. For him, the cuckoo simply didn't make any sense at all:

> The *Cuckow* her self builds no nest; but having found the nest of some little bird, she either devours or destroys the eggs she there finds, and in the room thereof lays one of her own, and so forsakes it. The silly bird returning, sits on this egg, hatches it, and with a great deal of care and toil broods, feeds and cherishes the young *Cuckow* for her own, until it be grown up and able to fly and shift for it self. Which thing seems so strange, monstrous and absurd, that for my part I cannot sufficiently wonder there should be such an example in nature; nor could I have ever been induced to believe such a thing had been done by natures instinct, had I not with my own eyes seen it. For nature in other things is wont constantly to observe one and the same law and

> order agreeable to the highest reason and prudence: Which in this case, is that dams make nests for themselves, if it need be, sit upon their own eggs, and bring up their young after they are hatched.

Perhaps it's not surprising, then, that early accounts suggested that there were abnormalities in cuckoo design. One view was that the cuckoo's parasitic behaviour was bestowed by a benevolent Creator to compensate for the lack of parental instincts. In *The Fowles of Heaven*, written in 1614, Edward Topsell expresses his admiration for

> that natural discretion with which the Grand Creator hath bestowed upon this siely fowle for the propagation of her oune kinde . . . it understandeth her oune frigiditie, or coldness of nature, utterly disabling it to hatche her oune kinde. Nature being defective in one part is wont to supply by another . . . want of streingth is recompenced with witt . . . the worke of God is wonderfull, and his mercy to his Creature magnificent.

Others thought that the cuckoo's defect lay not in its behaviour but rather in its anatomy. In 1752, the French anatomist François Hérissant noted that the cuckoo's stomach was unusually large and protruded low into the belly, and he suggested that if the female cuckoo were to sit on her eggs she would surely smash them. A few years later, in 1789, the famous British naturalist Gilbert White describes in his *Natural History of Selborne* how he dissected a cuckoo, concurring with Hérissant that: 'the crop placed just upon the bowels must, especially when full, be in a very uneasy situation during the business of incubation.' However, when he dissected some other species that did care for their young, including the nightjar and swift, he found that they too had cuckoo-like guts and concluded that:

> Monsieur Hérissant's conjecture, that cuckoos are incapsable of incubation from the disposition of their intestines, seems to fall to the ground; and we are still at a loss for the cause of that strange and singular peculiarity in the instance of the cuculus canorus.

Gilbert White regarded the cuckoo's habits as unnatural: 'a monstrous outrage on maternal affection, one of the first great dictates of nature'.

At about the same time that Gilbert White was cutting up cuckoos, Edward Jenner was testing Hérissant's theory by experiment. He placed two partly incubated pied wagtail eggs under a two-week-old cuckoo nestling that was being raised in a dunnock nest. A week later, the wagtail eggs hatched. Jenner concluded that if a young cuckoo could incubate eggs successfully then an adult cuckoo should be able to do so too. Instead he proposed another explanation for the cuckoo's parasitic habits, namely that its early departure from the breeding grounds at the beginning of July left no time for parental care and compelled it to be a parasite.

This argument seems odd today, now that we are familiar with the variable migratory habits of many species. Reed warblers, for example, if they fail to raise their late summer broods successfully, migrate several weeks earlier than those still busy raising young to independence. Jenner has surely got his argument back to front: the adult cuckoos choose to depart early precisely because they have no parental duties to perform. On Wicken Fen, their departure in early July coincides exactly with the time reed warblers cease to start new clutches, and so marks the end of the summer's opportunities for parasitism.

If early writers considered the cuckoo had to be a parasite to compensate for its bad design, how did they explain the host's acceptance of the cuckoo chick? A common suggestion was that this was an act of benevolence. For example, Bechstein, writing in 1791, thought that the hosts would be only too honoured to raise a cuckoo chick, rather than a brood of their own, and he mistook the host alarm calls for cries of glee:

> It is wonderful to observe what great apparent delight the birds show when they see a female cuckoo approach their abode. Instead of leaving their eggs, as they do when disturbed by the approach of other animals, they seem quite beside themselves for joy. The little wren, for example, when brooding over its own eggs, immediately quits its nest on the approach of the cuckoo, as though to make room to enable her to lay her egg more commodiously. Meanwhile she hops round her with such expressions of delight that her husband at length joins her, and both seem lavish in their thanks for the honour which the great bird confers upon them by selecting their nest for its own use.

In 1859, these quaint views, of bad cuckoo design and host benevolence, were swept away for ever by Charles Darwin. In chapter 8 of *The Origin of Species*, he discusses the parasitic habits of the common cuckoo as a prime example of how behaviour can evolve by natural selection. Darwin knew that some species of American cuckoos are not parasitic, but have normal parental behaviour. They build their own nests, incubate their eggs and raise their young to independence just like most birds. Back in

1794, this had been a source of pride for Charles Willson Peale, who created the Philadelphia Museum with admission tickets bearing the slogan 'The birds and beasts will teach thee.' He contrasted cuckoos from the Old World, 'notorious symbols of infidelity for their practice of planting their eggs in the nests of other birds', with cuckoos from America, with their admirable family values, and he was 'proud to believe that they are faithful and constant to each other'. However, Darwin learnt from his correspondents that these parental cuckoos were not so virtuous after all and occasionally laid eggs in the nests of other species. He then proposed this evolutionary sequence:

> Now let us suppose that the ancient progenitor of our European cuckoo had the habits of the American cuckoo, and that she occasionally laid an egg in another bird's nest. If the old bird profited by this occasional habit through being enabled to migrate earlier or through any other cause; or if the young were made more vigorous by advantage being taken of the mistaken instinct of another species than when reared by their own mother, encumbered as she could hardly fail to be by having eggs and young of different ages at the same time; then the old birds or the fostered young would gain an advantage. And analogy would lead us to believe, that the young thus reared would be apt to follow by inheritance the occasional and aberrant habit of their mother; and in their turn would be apt to lay their eggs in other birds' nests, and thus be more successful in rearing their young. By a continued process of this nature, I believe that the strange instinct of our cuckoo has been generated.

This paragraph still dazzles me with its originality, and even today biologists are busy investigating its three main suggestions.

Darwin's first point is that far from being defective behaviour, parasitic laying can be a positive advantage and bring better reproductive success than parental care. Relieved of the time and energy commitment of parental duties, a parasitic adult could indeed migrate earlier; but more importantly, we might add, it could use the saved resources to lay more eggs per season. In fact we now know that parasitic cuckoos are especially prolific in their laying. A parental cuckoo might have time to raise at most two clutches in a season, each of three eggs. The parasitic common cuckoo, laying one egg in each host nest, lays an average of eight eggs per season, while many individuals lay 15 or more and the maximum recorded from one female is 25. Similarly, another parasitic bird in North America, the brown-headed cowbird, can lay 40 eggs or more per season, compared with two clutches of four for a typical parental species in this same family of American blackbirds. Furthermore, as Darwin points out, common cuckoo chicks are raised alone in the host nest and so escape competition for food. Perhaps they grow better than they would if reared in a brood by their own parents. Far from being defective, therefore, parasitic laying seems positively advantageous. So the worry of Gilbert White and Edward Jenner should really be turned on its head: why haven't more species become parasitic, to exploit the workforce of so many honest parental species?

According to the latest estimate, there are about 10,000 species of birds in the world. Precise estimates vary depending on how full species are separated from subspecies, exactly the kind of uncertainty predicted by evolutionary change, because divergence between species is a gradual process, not a sudden event. Of these, 102 species are obligate brood parasites; that is to say, they always lay eggs in the nests of other species and rely on these as hosts to incubate their eggs and raise their young. The parasites comprise 59 species of parasitic cuckoos (Cuculidae), five species of parasitic cowbirds (Icteridae), 17 species of honey-guides (Indicatoridae), 20 species of African parasitic finches (Estrildidae) and one duck (the black-headed duck from South America). Clearly, success as a parasite depends on a good supply of host species. But if, as Darwin suggests, brood parasitism is so advantageous, why have only 1 per cent of all bird species evolved this lifestyle?

Darwin's second suggestion is that parasitic laying evolved gradually from parental ancestry. He had no direct evidence and simply argued that it was plausible for occasional parasitic behaviour to evolve, by stages, into full-time parasitism. However, we now know that this conjecture is correct. In 2005, Michael Sorenson and Robert Payne constructed a family tree for the 141 species of cuckoo in the world (family Cuculidae), based on similarities in their DNA. Only 42 per cent of cuckoo species are parasitic (59 species); the other 58 per cent (82 species) are parental species. The tree shows clearly that within the cuckoo family parasitic laying has evolved independently three times from parental ancestry: once in South American cuckoos (three related species in the genera *Tapera* and *Dromococcyx*), once in the crested cuckoos of Eurasia and Africa (four species in the genus *Clamator*), and once in another large group of parasites (52 species in 11 related genera, including our common cuckoo in the genus *Cuculus*).

Darwin's third point is the one that has fascinated me for the last 30 years. It's that hosts don't raise cuckoos through benevolence, of course. How could they? Any reed warbler that spent its time preferring to raise cuckoos instead of its own young would fail to pass on those generous instincts to future generations. On the other hand, a reed warbler that refused to raise cuckoos and focused on raising its own young would pass on its selfish instincts to those offspring, so the selfish raising of one's own young (or other genetic relatives) should be the habit we'd most expect to see throughout nature. And indeed it is. Darwin's idea to explain acceptance of a cuckoo chick is simply that the hosts get tricked, or follow what he calls 'a mistaken instinct'. 'Wonderful and admirable as most instincts are,' he wrote, 'yet they cannot be considered as absolutely perfect; there is a constant struggle going on throughout nature between the instinct of the one to escape its enemy and of the other to secure its prey.' Darwin likened the natural world to an entangled bank, where each species was forever evolving new defences or new tricks to combat its ever-changing competitors and enemies.

In theory, then, we should expect there to be what Richard Dawkins and John Krebs have termed an 'evolutionary arms race' between cuckoos and hosts. In response to parasitism by cuckoos, hosts should evolve defences, such as protecting their nests against laying cuckoos, and rejecting cuckoo eggs and cuckoo chicks. In turn, this would lead to the evolution of better trickery by cuckoos to beat host defences. Better cuckoo trickery would then favour the evolution of even better host defence, leading to further improvements in cuckoo trickery, further improvements in host defences, and so on. In other words, hosts and cuckoos should co-evolve, with changes in either party selecting for changes in the other party.

Are cuckoos and host evolving together in such an arms race?

A week later, I return to the reed warbler nest on Wicken Fen. Once more, I part the reeds with my stick. At first, I don't see the cuckoo. The vegetation has grown and it takes my eyes time to adjust to the bright sunlight reflected from the stems and leaves. But suddenly there it is, sitting perfectly still in the depths of the reeds. The cuckoo is now three weeks old, much larger than before, with longer wings and tail, and it seems ready to fledge. The nest is in a sorry state. It is flattened, and one of the supports has become detached from the reeds. The cuckoo now perches on the ragged remains of the rim. I notice its toes, two pointing forwards and two back, the typical arrangement of all members of the cuckoo family. This time I daren't approach closely in case it flies off. I retreat, sit back on the bank and peer through the narrow gap in the reeds. I can just make out the head and front part of the body, but it is hard to see in the dark interior. All is still and quiet and I become distracted by the dragonflies patrolling along the edge of the ditch; male four-spotted chasers defending their mating territories. For some fen creatures the summer has just begun.

A frenzy of calling '*tsi . . . tsi . . . tsi . . .*' and I look towards the cuckoo once more. A reed warbler lands on the cuckoo's back! The cuckoo turns it head and the warbler deposits a large black and yellow hoverfly deep into the enormous gape. This time the warbler's head disappears completely, and for a moment I imagine that the cuckoo will swallow its host whole. But the feed is over in a couple of seconds, the warbler darts off through the reeds and the cuckoo becomes still and silent once more.

At that moment, Darwin's suggestion that the hosts have been tricked seems to me more unlikely than ever. The cuckoo chick is now eight times the weight of the reed warbler. Surely a parent that has to perch on the back of such a monstrous chick in order to deliver a feed should realise something is amiss. Have reed warblers any defences against cuckoos? If so, how does the cuckoo chick manage to fool them so easily? To begin to answer these questions, we have to go back to the start of the summer to discover how the cuckoo lays her egg.

2

How the cuckoo lays her egg

Female cuckoo gliding down to lay her egg in a meadow pipit nest.
23 June 2014.

Another summer's day, nearly 100 years ago. A vintage motor-car draws up gently at the edge of a small patch of heathland in the Wyre Forest, Worcestershire, England. A well-dressed gentleman emerges from the driver's seat. He is wearing a flat tweed cap, tweed jacket and waistcoat with white shirt and tie, and his trousers are 'plus-fours', baggy knickerbockers with thick woollen socks up to his knees. Two other men get out, not quite so smart but still in clean white shirts (no tie) and jackets. They go round to the back of the car. An observer might expect them to bring out a hamper for a picnic. But what emerges from the luggage compartment is a surprise: a little hut, as tall as a man, made from bundles of twigs and heather, wrapped around a wicker frame.

The trio walk slowly across the heath, the gentleman in the lead, peering intently at the ground, with the two men behind, carrying the twig hut. Suddenly, the gentleman stops and he points ahead with his walking stick. The two men lower the hut to the ground. It is in two halves, and they remove the top. The gentleman steps inside and is handed a little stool. The top is replaced, and after a few moments a hand appears from a gap in the twig wall and gives a friendly wave. A few adjustments to make sure the hut is secure, then the two men retreat, leaving the smart gentleman hidden inside.

This is Pound Green Common, and we have been watching the start of a 12-minute silent black-and-white film, *The Cuckoo's Secret*, made in 1921. The smart gentleman is Edgar Chance, and

Edgar Chance getting into his hide on Pound Green Common in 1920, assisted by Simmonds father and son. Photo by Oliver G. Pike, The Truth About the Cuckoo, *Edgar Chance.*

the film celebrates his discovery of how the cuckoo lays her egg. This was one of the earliest wildlife films ever made, and it became the first of a celebrated series called 'Secrets of Life'. It was shown to great acclaim at packed picture-houses across Britain and then in New York. The film is remarkable not only because it captures, for the very first time, a cuckoo laying in a host nest, but also because the cinematographer, Edward Hawkins, was a newsreel cameraman with no previous experience of wildlife filming. As Edgar Chance recalls in his 1940 book *The Truth About the Cuckoo*, when he met Hawkins for the first time at the train station:

> Hawkins told me with some appreciation of his responsibility that he had never seen a cuckoo in his life. I put him at ease by replying that all that mattered was his ability

faithfully to film what he would see, and promising him that he would see what no one else had ever seen.

As we watch the film, then, we can share Hawkins's excitement as he in turn sat with his camera in the twiggy bird hide on Pound Green Common, just a few metres from a meadow pipit nest, which was on the ground by a tuft of grass. First, we see the female cuckoo laying an egg. What is most astonishing about this is the speed; she flies down to the pipit nest, lays her egg and departs, all within eight seconds. Chance had been watching the cuckoo from the edge of the Common and as soon as she flew towards the nest, he alerted Hawkins in the hide with the blast of a whistle to ensure the camera was running to catch this sequence.

Twelve days later, as the caption on the film explains, the cuckoo egg has hatched and the cuckoo chick, naked and blind, finds itself sharing the nest with two newly hatched pipit chicks and one unhatched pipit egg. Next, we see the mother pipit brooding. Suddenly, she is pushed aside and from beneath her the cuckoo chick emerges, shuffling backwards and struggling to balance the pipit egg in between its wing stumps in a little hollow in the middle of its back. The cuckoo backs up to the rim of the nest and pushes the egg overboard, with a final flick of its wings. The mother pipit looks on, apparently unconcerned, while the cuckoo sinks back into the nest.

After a while, the mother leaves on a foraging trip. While she is away, the cuckoo turns its attention to one of the young pipits. Now balancing this on its back, it works its way slowly up the side of the nest once more, pushing with its strong legs. It tries repeatedly to eject the pipit chick, but a writhing chick is harder to control than an egg and a minute later it is still heaving away as the parent pipit returns. She ignores the commotion on the edge of the nest and instead feeds the other pipit chick with a caterpillar. The cuckoo, apparently exhausted, slides back into the nest, together with its load, and the mother sits on all three chicks once more to keep them warm.

The mother leaves again. While she is away, the cuckoo chick, now recovered, quickly ejects the two pipits in turn, one by one. The pipit chicks writhe helplessly for a while on the ground just outside the nest, and when the parent pipit returns it feeds one of them with a caterpillar. But then it sits on the cuckoo chick inside the nest and pays no more attention to its own two young, still writhing just a few centimetres away over the rim. They slowly chill and are left to perish while the adult pipits tend the cuckoo, which has taken sole command of the nest. We watch the pipits working hard to feed the cuckoo, first as a growing nestling and then, after it leaves the nest, as an enormous fledgling.

These sequences must have both astonished and shocked viewers. The film captions perhaps convey the public reaction at the time: they refer to the cuckoo as 'the feathered wrecker of homes', who 'shirks the duties of a mother bird'. What makes the film remarkable is the detective work necessary to catch the cuckoo laying her egg. Chance not only had to predict which pipit nest the cuckoo would choose, he had to know what day the female would lay, and at exactly what time, so he would be there to capture the drama in those crucial eight seconds. How did he do it?

Edgar Chance was a businessman, director of a company of glass manufacturers in Birmingham. But his passion was oology, the collecting and study of birds' eggs. Before he began his studies on

Pound Green Common, previous egg collectors had shown that the eggs of the common cuckoo are astonishingly variable. In Europe, most are speckled but the background colour varies: various shades of greyish-white, green or brown. The markings vary too: small speckles, large spots and even scribbles. Some have no markings at all and are plain white or an immaculate pale blue. No other bird in Europe has such variable eggs.

Whenever collectors found a cuckoo egg, they took the whole clutch to show the cuckoo egg alongside the host eggs. It had long been known (since at least the last half of the eighteenth century) that the cuckoo egg tended to resemble the host eggs, though it was a little larger. In Britain, for example, cuckoo eggs in reed warbler nests are greenish and spotted like those of the reed warbler. In meadow pipit nests, the cuckoo egg is darker, brown and speckled, matching the pipit's own eggs. In pied wagtail nests, the cuckoo egg is much paler, a greyish-white and finely speckled, just like the wagtail's eggs. In other parts of Europe the matches are even more impressive. Cuckoo eggs in redstart nests are immaculate pale blue, a perfect match for the host eggs, and in great reed warbler nests they have a pale green background with spots of various sizes and shades, from pale blue-grey to dark brown, which copy to perfection the markings on the host's eggs.

Could a female cuckoo vary the colour of her egg depending on the host she chose? This seemed most unlikely. Although a female's egg might vary a little depending on her diet, the variation in cuckoo eggs was surely too great to be in the repertoire of an individual female. In 1892, two German oologists, Eduard Baldamus and Eugene Rey, both collected series of eggs from individual females, laid in adjacent host nests in a restricted territory. Their collections showed that each female always laid exactly the same type of egg. Furthermore, they discovered that different females preferred different hosts; some might target reed warblers, for example, while others targeted meadow pipits. Occasionally they found that a female laid an egg in the nest of the 'wrong' host species, perhaps when a nest of her favourite host was not available. But she still laid exactly the same egg each time.

These pioneering studies by egg collectors showed, therefore, that the match between cuckoo and host egg must come about because female cuckoos with different egg types somehow managed to choose the host species for which their egg was a good match. The alternative possibility was that cuckoos simply laid eggs at random and only well-matched eggs survived for the egg collectors to record. It was already known that birds sometimes rejected a foreign egg placed in their nest. However, random egg laying followed by host rejection seemed an unlikely explanation for the match between cuckoo and host eggs, because many cuckoo eggs were collected soon after they were laid, and random laying would be extremely wasteful from the cuckoo's point of view. In any case, Baldamus and Rey had shown that individual female cuckoos did not lay eggs randomly, but rather favoured one host species.

These observations suggested that the common cuckoo must be divided into several races, each specialising in a particular host species, and laying distinctive eggs that matched its host's eggs: brown and spotted for meadow pipit specialist cuckoos, green and spotted for reed warbler specialists, plain blue for redstart specialists, and so on. In 1893, Alfred Newton called these cuckoo races *gentes* (*gens* in the singular), a Latin word denoting a clan of families descended from a common ancestor. We now know that there are genetic differences between the cuckoo races, so they are rather like subspecies of the common cuckoo.

Edgar Chance admired these previous studies by Eugene Rey

and others, but what really fired his obsessive passion for collecting was when he heard that Rey had a record series of 20 eggs laid by a female cuckoo in one season, near Leipzig. (In fact, Chance had been misinformed; Rey's series was of 17 eggs, still a tribute to the success of the parasitic lifestyle.) Chance was determined to beat this record. To be sure of collecting all a female cuckoo's eggs in one season, however, he would have to follow her carefully to discover not only every host nest she chose, but exactly when laying occurred. He also knew of an egg collector's trick which might entice a cuckoo into laying more eggs, so he could beat Rey.

There was another motivation for Chance's study, a dispute that he wanted to settle once and for all. Some observers claimed that the female cuckoo first laid her egg on the ground and then inserted it into the host nest with her bill. These were the 'beakers'. Others, the 'regurgitators', thought the cuckoo arrived at the host nest with her egg in her oesophagus, and then regurgitated it into the nest. There seemed to be good evidence for these possibilities: female cuckoos had indeed often been seen flying past with an egg in their bill, and some female cuckoos that had been shot had been found with an egg in their throats. Furthermore, some hosts, such as the wren, have a domed nest with a tiny hole for an entrance. Surely the female cuckoo could not lay directly into these nests. Eugene Rey, for example, was a 'beaker', citing a cuckoo egg found in the nest of a red-backed shrike that was smeared with clay as proof that the egg had first been on the ground. Chance was convinced both parties were wrong, and that the female cuckoo laid directly into the host nest, just like other birds. This was his second incentive to discover exactly when and where the cuckoo laid, so he could catch her in the act.

Pound Green Common was an isolated patch of undulating grassland and heather, about 400 × 600 metres, and bounded on three sides by woodland. It was a man-made common, cleared for grazing in the eighteenth century, which then provided ideal habitat for meadow pipits and other ground-nesting species – tree pipits, skylarks, yellowhammers and stonechats. It had a few scattered tall trees, perfect lookout posts for female cuckoos searching for host nests. Chance's most detailed work on the common was during the five summers from 1918 to 1922. Together with his four assistants, O. R. Owen, P. B. Smyth and the two Simmondses, a local coal miner and his son, he began a regular routine of searching for host nests. By clever detective work from collecting cuckoo and host eggs, they slowly pieced together the remarkable story of how the cuckoo lays her eggs.

The first summer, 1918, Britain was still at war and it was possible to make only casual visits to the common. When Chance first visited, at the end of May, breeding had already been under way for a month. He soon discovered how hard it was to find nests in the dense vegetation. Pipit nests were on the ground and often tucked away out of sight in little hollows, under tufts of grass or clumps of heather, and even when the collie dog of the elder Simmonds flushed a sitting bird close by their feet, they often failed to find the nest. They often heard male cuckoos calling, '*cuck-oo*', and also the bubbling cries of females, best described as a 'water-bubbling chuckle'. On some days they saw a female glide down from a tree perch to the ground, but it was usually impossible to locate the exact spot she had landed. Despite these early frustrations, the team found eggs from two female cuckoos that summer. Both laid the brown eggs typical for cuckoos of the meadow pipit race, but each female's eggs were distinguishable by slight differences in their ground shade and markings. One, 'Cuckoo A', laid her eggs on one side of the common, 10 eggs in the nests of meadow pipits and one in a skylark's nest. The other, 'Cuckoo B', laid her eggs in an adjacent territory on the other side, just four eggs, all in meadow pipit nests.

Chance collected all these cuckoo and host eggs and to preserve them he blew out their contents by making a tiny hole at each end of the egg. By examining the embryos, he could determine the stage of incubation. In each parasitised clutch, cuckoo and host egg had about the same stage of development, so Chance concluded that the cuckoo must time the laying of her egg in each nest to coincide with the days the hosts laid. Meadow pipits usually lay a clutch of four or five eggs, one per day. So the cuckoo has only a short window of opportunity, just four or five days at each host nest. To parasitise 10 or more nests in a season, she must have to watch all the hosts carefully to get her timing right. In future, Chance determined to watch the cuckoos as well as search for host nests.

The next season was eagerly awaited. Meadow pipits were clearly the favoured host, but in the spring of 1919 there were only 10 pairs on the common, so Chance decided to give the cuckoos a helping hand. In early May, just before the cuckoos arrived, he collected all the pipit clutches that were already being incubated and so were too late for parasitism. These pairs immediately began to build new nests, and within seven or eight days they had begun a replacement clutch, so the result was more pipits at the right stage for the early cuckoo eggs. To Chance's delight, the same two female cuckoos returned, recognisable by their characteristic eggs, and they laid in exactly the same, adjacent territories as the previous year. During this second season, 18 eggs were collected from Cuckoo A, all from meadow pipit nests, even though there were many skylarks, tree pipits and linnets nesting in her territory, showing convincingly that she was a host specialist. Only two eggs were found from Cuckoo B, both again in meadow pipit nests.

By checking nests daily, to determine exactly when the cuckoo egg was laid, and then again later to determine exactly when it hatched, Chance calculated that the cuckoo hatched after only 12 days' incubation, compared with 13 days for the host eggs. Therefore, provided the female cuckoo timed the laying of her egg correctly, the shorter incubation time gave the cuckoo chick the chance to eject the host eggs before they hatched, likely to be an easier task than ejecting struggling host chicks.

Chance was now able to estimate the laying dates for the few cuckoo eggs that he had failed to find until after incubation had begun. The sequence from Cuckoo A, which he was sure were all the eggs that she had laid that summer, showed that she laid on alternate days. The first five were laid in this regular sequence from 18 to 26 May. Then there was a three-day gap. The next 13 were laid on alternate days from 30 May to 23 June.

Chance had, in fact, beaten Rey's record of 17 eggs in a season by one, but his misinformation led him to believe that he was still three eggs short. So in the third season, 1920, he decided to increase the availability of pipit nests still further by 'farming' both parasitised and unparasitised clutches throughout the season to make sure there would always be a suitable nest available for the cuckoo whenever she needed one. If a pipit had an empty nest on the day a cuckoo was due to lay, Chance added an egg or two, from another pipit or skylark nest, to make the nest appear as if laying had begun. To his relief, Cuckoo A returned once more. This time, with Chance's help, she laid a total of 21 eggs, 20 in meadow pipit nests and one in the nest of a tree pipit, and his 'world record' was secure.

This third season had revealed more about cuckoo behaviour, too. As Chance checked each host nest, he often flushed Cuckoo A from a nearby tree and realised that she was busy doing the same thing! So the easiest way to find host nests was simply to watch her. 'By enlisting the cuckoo as a member of our band of observers,' Chance wrote, 'we could make her do much of the donkey work.'

By the end of May 1920, Cuckoo A had already laid 10 eggs. Chance knew she laid on alternate days, so by careful farming of clutches to restart nests in rotation, at two-day intervals, he could be fairly sure which nest she would choose. But still he had failed to witness the laying event itself. At first he assumed that the cuckoo would lay early in the morning, just as the pipits did. So he stayed out all night on the common to make sure he was at the host nest at dawn, but when he checked the nest he was surprised to find that the cuckoo had already laid her egg. Next time he got there even earlier. One cold and misty morning, he awoke at 3.45 a.m. to find a new cuckoo egg alongside a pipit egg, both cold and damp and clearly unattended during the night (pipits do not begin incubation until the clutch is complete, or nearly so). He suddenly realised his mistake: the cuckoo must have laid her egg the previous afternoon.

With the discovery of this final piece of the cuckoo's timing puzzle, the team of observers now focused their attention on the female cuckoo every afternoon. At last they were able to watch her lay, most often between 3 p.m. and 6 p.m. Beforehand, she would remain motionless on a branch, hidden in a tree up to 100 metres from the host nest. This could be an agonising wait for Chance and his team; sometimes she sat there for 30 minutes, sometimes for two and a half hours. Then, when she was ready, she glided down to the nest, remained there for usually just 10 seconds or so, and left. When the observers checked the nest, they found one host egg missing and the cuckoo egg in its place. Incredibly, she had removed a host egg and laid her own all in just a few seconds. But still no one had seen exactly how she laid.

Cuckoo A returned again in 1921, and in this her fourth season, Chance was triumphant at last. He now knew the days the female would lay (every other day), could predict which nest she was likely to choose (one where the pipits were still laying), could limit the cuckoo's choice (by farming pipit clutches so there was just one suitable nest available that day), and knew the time she would lay (late afternoon). So by placing hides close to the predicted host nest he was able to watch the cuckoo lay from just a few metres away.

This is what he saw. As soon as she landed by the nest, the female removed a host egg. Then, holding this in her bill, she sat briefly on the nest to lay her own. She then backed off and flew away, carrying the host egg. On landing on a nearby perch, she then swallowed the host egg whole. These observations solved two puzzles at once. The female laid her egg directly in the nest, just like other birds do. And the egg that previous observers had seen the female carry in her bill was a host egg, not the cuckoo's egg. The beakers and regurgitators had got it wrong. We now know that direct laying is the normal procedure for common cuckoos with all their hosts. For those with domed nests, like wrens, the female simply clings to the nest, places her belly against the nest hole, and squirts the egg in.

It was during this fourth season that Edward Hawkins was hired to film the laying for the first time. He obtained the best sequences during the laying of the second, third, fourth, twelfth, thirteenth and fourteenth eggs, and the best approach glide of the cuckoo to the pipit nest with the laying of the seventh egg. It is remarkable that Chance was able to predict so well which nests would be chosen, so that hides could be placed correctly for Hawkins to catch so many layings. The result was an edited film that could show all the stages in wonderful detail.

In mid-June 1921, Chance stopped collecting completed host clutches. Without his help to make more nests available, Cuckoo A laid fewer eggs that summer, just 15 in total: 14 in meadow pipit nests and one in a tree pipit nest. This showed very neatly that a cuckoo's output on the common was limited more by the availability of host nests than by food to form the eggs.

Cuckoo A's fifth and final season in 1922 was, in Chance's own words, 'an outstanding and historic performance'. With human help restored, to make available as many host nests as possible, and including the additional trick of putting out extra artificial nests next to occupied ones, she achieved a total of 25 eggs that summer, all collected by Chance. All were laid in meadow pipit nests, and they involved just 11 pairs of pipits, some having their clutches farmed by Chance several times. Some of these layings were filmed from a hide by a second cameraman engaged by Chance, Oliver Pike, using what for the time was 'ultra-rapid' film, to illustrate the laying sequence. Guests, too, were invited to watch the egg laying. Chance records that 'Mrs. Pike got very excited inside the hide, while watching the cuckoo lay, despite the fact that she had had considerable experience of bird-watching.' However, not all shared such enthusiasm or patience, and some nodded off in the warmth of the hide during the crucial 10 seconds.

Chance published his discoveries in two books: *The Cuckoo's Secret* in 1922 and then an expanded version in 1940, *The Truth About the Cuckoo*, which recorded the egg-laying exploits of five other cuckoos on the common, up to 1930. These five females were all meadow pipit specialists, just like Cuckoo A. Chance's meticulous records, from all the cuckoos he followed, totalled 86 eggs: 71 laid in meadow pipit nests, eight in tree pipit nests, four in a yellowhammer nest, and one each in the nests of skylark, willow warbler and linnet. His books have black and white photographs by Oliver Pike, so we can see Cuckoo A in action: landing by the host nest, leaning in to pick out a host egg, sitting in the nest to lay, backing out, and then flying off with the host egg in her bill. Some of the stills taken from the cine film are small and blurry, and Chance recommends the reader to use a magnifying glass. But these are the remarkable first records of exactly how the cuckoo lays her eggs.

Cuckoo A parasitising a meadow pipit nest on Pound Green Common in 1922. First, she picks out one of the host's eggs. Holding it in her beak, she then lays her own egg directly into the nest.

Cuckoo A then flies off with the host egg.
These were the first-ever photographs of a cuckoo laying her egg. Photos by Oliver G. Pike, The Truth About the Cuckoo, *Edgar Chance.*

Chapter 7 of *The Truth About the Cuckoo* records, in remarkable and loving detail, the laying of every egg from Cuckoo A's record-breaking performance during the summer of 1922, from her first on 11 May to her twenty-fifth on 29 June. With just one extra day's break after the second egg, she laid them on alternate days: May 11, 13, 16, 18, 20, 22, 24, 26, 28, 30, June 1, 3, 5, 7, 9, 11, 13, 15, 17, 19, 21, 23, 25, 27 and 29. It is difficult to decide who is more deserving of our admiration: the cuckoo, for keeping track of so many host nests, so she could time the laying of each egg to coincide with the pipit's own egg-laying period, or Chance and his team, for managing to keep up with her. His account of the laying of the sixth egg conveys all the thrills and frustrations of trying to predict which pipit nest the female would choose:

> *May 22*: Present were the Rev. Allan Ellison, the Hon. Guy Charteris, Oliver Pike, the two Simmondses and myself. The expected nest was 3a, but there were other possibilities . . . At 11 a.m. the cuckoo was watching 6b . . . for thirty-five minutes we watched her sit motionless, then she flew away . . . from 2.15 to 2.45 we sheltered from a heavy thunderstorm in hides . . . We resumed our vigil at 2.45 . . . Ellison was posted fifteen yards from 3a nest and Pike in the sand-pit to watch 4a and 5 territories. Charteris, with either Simmonds or myself, was guarding the territories of 6a and b6 [*sic*], the nest of the latter not yet found. There was no sign or sound of the cuckoo, but exactly at 4 p.m. Ellison whistled, and on Pike's advice I went over . . . only to realise Ellison had only seen the cuckoo *leave* the nest. My dear friend admitted having felt sleepy because of the sultry heat. Thus I experienced the annoyance caused by the failure of a privileged guest to rise to the occasion after I had stationed him in the most favourable position!

Chance was proud of his season's record from Cuckoo A, though he admitted it was achieved largely as a result of his help by the continuous collection of clutches to 'restart' the pipits. He marvelled at the observation skills of the female cuckoo, who obviously had kept an eye on his nest manipulations throughout the summer, so she could take advantage of the extra laying opportunities he arranged for her. Surely nature, unguided, would never provide so many laying opportunities. Chance believed that his record would 'never be equalled so long as cuckoos continue to lay'.

However, Chance underestimated the cuckoo's cunning. He knew that cuckoos would sometimes eat whole clutches of host eggs that were too advanced for parasitism, but subsequent studies have shown that this is a regular strategy used by female cuckoos to restart the hosts. In a study from 1970 to 1981 of cuckoos parasitising marsh warblers, near Hamburg, Germany, Karsten Gärtner found that 30 per cent of host nests with completed clutches or young chicks were taken by female cuckoos. In another study of cuckoos parasitising reed warblers in France, cuckoos laid more than a quarter of their eggs in replacement nests following such predation. Only female cuckoos, not males, plunder host nests, so it is a strategy to increase the availability of host nests, not simply a hungry cuckoo looking for an easy meal.

Unwittingly, then, Chance had simply been doing what cuckoos normally do for themselves. The female cuckoo is not only a superb watcher of the host nests in her territory, she is an arch manipulator too, taking clutches to stagger host laying and so maximise her egg-laying opportunities throughout the season. In 1988, a cuckoo studied by Mike Bayliss in Oxfordshire, central England, equalled Cuckoo A's record without human help. She parasitised a population of 36 pairs of reed warblers, laying 25 eggs in the season and parasitising 24 of the pairs, one pair twice.

Over her five seasons on Pound Green Common, Cuckoo A laid 90 eggs, all collected by Chance except for the few that hatched before he found them. Eighty-seven had been laid in meadow pipit nests, two in tree pipit nests and one in a skylark nest. They are now beautifully displayed in wooden cabinets in the Natural History Museum at Tring in Hertfordshire, with Chance's neat labels and numbers on each egg in the sequence, a testament to his extraordinary obsession. Cuckoo A paid a price:

her five long trips across the Sahara to her African winter quarters and back, and five summers' work finding all those pipit nests, led to no genetic immortality. But the cuckoo's laying secret, a mystery since the time of Aristotle, was a story told by her eggshells. Her memory endures in those lifeless jewels.

Edgar Chance died in 1955 at the age of 74, having amassed a collection of 25,000 bird eggs. Egg collecting from common birds, which included the cuckoo in those days, was not illegal, but Chance collected the eggs of rare, protected species too. In April 1926 he was fined 13 pounds and 10 shillings for unlawfully taking crossbill eggs, and was expelled from the British Ornithologists' Union. He dedicated his second cuckoo book to his daughter, Ann Augusta Cardamine, named after lady's smock, *Cardamine pratensis*, also called the cuckooflower because its delicate, pale pink flowers first bloom towards the end of April, at about the time the cuckoo returns to Britain to breed.

In June 2008 I made a pilgrimage to Pound Green Common. Some of the landmarks in Chance's 1921 film were still clear: a little hut and the rough track where he drove in with his hide on the back of his motorcar. But, with a decline in sheep grazing, the common had now become overgrown with bracken, silver birch and oak scrub. There were no meadow pipits, just a lone tree pipit singing for a mate from the top of a birch tree.

I sat on the edge of the common and imagined Edgar Chance working here 90 years ago in his tweed suit and tie. His careful observations and his brilliant solving, piece by piece, of the cuckoo's secret surely must rank as one of the greatest feats in field ornithology. My mind wandered and then, from the distant pine plantation, I thought I heard a male cuckoo call, just a few times and very faint. I stood, cupped my hands and blew a loud reply: '*cuck-oo*, *cuck-oo*'. All was silent and I sat down again. Perhaps I had been fooled by a pilgrim's daydreams. A minute later, however, a cuckoo suddenly appeared, flying fast and low towards me, just over my head. I called again and he circled the common twice, calling '*cuck-oo*' and making a low, guttural '*kwow-wow-wow*', as if in annoyance at the intrusion. Then he perched at the top of a tall birch tree, with his tail held high and his wings drooped, twisting from side to side and calling loudly, without pausing, '*cuck-oo*, *cuck-oo*'. I let him call there, unanswered, for a few minutes. Then, apparently satisfied that the intruder had been beaten off, he flew back to the distant plantation.

Members of the local Commoners' Association plan to clear the bracken and birches, and they hope that with restoration of the lowland heath, with its grassland and heather, both meadow pipits and cuckoos will return. But that day, once the cuckoo had left, I sat alone on a silent common, saluting the memory of Edgar Chance.

3

Wicken Fen

Barn owl hunting over Wicken Fen at dusk.
10 May 2014.

Edgar Chance had shown beautifully *how* the female common cuckoo lays her eggs. I wanted to discover *why* she behaves in this particular way. Has the cuckoo evolved tricks to try to beat host defences? Are cuckoos and hosts engaged in a continuing evolutionary arms race?

When I was a student, one of my tutors warned me: 'The days when you can go out into the countryside with binoculars and notebook and discover something interesting are long gone.' By this he was implying that scientific progress often depends on new techniques. For example, since the 1980s new and powerful methods of DNA profiling have been developed which allow us to determine paternity and maternity in wild populations. These have revolutionised studies of animal mating systems, revealing that socially monogamous birds are not the models of fidelity that we had once assumed.

But sometimes progress is made not through new techniques but through new ideas, or simply by asking new questions. Darwin's idea that cuckoos are exploiting the 'mistaken instincts' of their hosts immediately raises new questions. How do hosts recognise their own eggs and chicks? What is it about cuckoo eggs and chicks that leads to mistaken acceptance? Patient observations with binoculars and notebook can still provide a fresh look at the natural world and lead to new discoveries, provided that the new questions are interesting. I felt sure that cuckoo–host interactions would be a fascinating corner of Darwin's 'entangled bank', and one that could be untangled by simple field experiments.

So I'm back on Wicken Fen once more. It is mid-April and I'm preparing for the summer's fieldwork. There is a cold north wind, which has kept the migrants at bay. But soon the cuckoos and reed warblers will be arriving from Africa, and before they set up their territories I need to mark out mine. This has been my spring routine every year since 1985 and I feel completely at home here under the huge skies. I walk along the reed-fringed waterways and every 20 paces attach small numbered tags to the reeds. These will help me plot the positions of all the reed warbler nests later, when the breeding season gets under way. Back in my garden in Cambridge, blackbirds, robins and dunnocks are already incubating clutches or feeding nestlings, but spring comes much later out in the fens. The new reeds are beginning to show green, just above the water surface, but they are sparse and the reed beds still have the mood of winter, dominated by the yellow-brown stems from last year's growth. The old fluffy seed heads shimmer silver as I walk into the early morning sunlight, and then gold as I wend my way home in the evening, with the sun behind me.

Common reeds are the tallest of Britain's native grasses and can reach three metres high. They grow as rhizomes underground, spreading through the soil and sending up new vertical shoots year after year, perhaps for centuries. While the rhizomes endure, these 'reeds' above ground die each autumn, though their dead stems may remain standing for several years. The old reeds will provide cover and nest sites for early reed warbler nests. In a week or so, these ditches will be full of singing reed warblers – and I wonder if the birds will derive the same satisfaction as I do from marking out a territory for the summer. With all my numbered tags in place,

I feel these ditches are mine for the season, that I have taken possession of the fen.

A few thousand years ago, the spring migrants would have met a different landscape. They would have dropped from the night skies into a huge wetland of some 4,000 square kilometres. This formed during the last 4,500 years, in the flood plain of the four great rivers flowing out into the Wash: the Witham, the Welland, the Nene and the Great Ouse. The vast flood plain was bordered by an upland arc, which stretched from Lincolnshire, north of the Wash, south to Cambridgeshire and Suffolk and then round to the southern edge of the Wash in Norfolk.

During the last ice age, more water was locked up as ice, and sea levels were therefore much lower than they are today. So if we go back some 10,000 years, before the fens were formed, this whole area would have been woodland, where brown bears, wild boar, aurochs and elk would have roamed. As the glaciers receded, rising sea levels began to impede the flow of the rivers out to the sea, and flooding led to the creation of wetlands. The forests slowly died and sank beneath the waterlogged soils. The northern part, nearest the Wash, was inundated periodically by estuarine silts from the North Sea, while further inland peat formed in fresh water as dead marshland vegetation accumulated.

The old fens must have been a wild and wonderful place. One of the earliest descriptions comes from *c.*740, in the *Life of Saint Guthlac*, written by Felix the monk, within 30 years of the saint's death:

> There is in the midland district of Britain a most dismal fen of immense size, which begins at the banks of the river

> Granta [Cam], not far from the camp which is called Cambridge, and stretches from the south as far north as the sea. It is a very long tract, now consisting of marshes, now of bogs, sometimes of black waters overhung by fog, sometimes studded with wooded islands and traversed by the windings of tortuous streams.

Guthlac retired to live an austere life on a lonely island in the fens (now the village of Crowland, Lincolnshire). The Guthlac poem, written in Old English, provides the first written record of the cuckoo in Britain:

> Thus that gentle heart cut itself off from the pleasures of mankind and served the Lord and he found his delight in wild creatures, once he had rejected the world. The site of his triumph and his lodgings were peaceful anew, the singing of the birds was lovely, the countryside was sprung into blossom and cuckoos heralded the year.

In the Middle Ages, people living in the fens were a tough breed. They wore furs made from otter, beaver and mole skins and were rumoured to have webbed feet. They travelled around the marshes on stilts, ice skates and punts, and made a living by trapping wildfowl, eels and fish. It was here, during the eleventh century, that Hereward the Wake (who lived from about 1035 to 1072) and his followers provided the last of the old English resistance against the Norman Conquest, hiding away in the depths of the fens after their raids against the invaders. Some of Hereward's fiercest battles were fought in the marshes around Ely, just north of Wicken.

The recent history of the fens is largely one of their destruction. The first attempts to drain the fens were in Roman times.

But drainage began in earnest in 1630, when King Charles I invited Cornelius Vermuyden to bring his engineering skills from the Netherlands. The draining was funded by a group of wealthy landowners, the 'Adventurers', led by the Earl of Bedford, all keen to make a profit from agriculture in the rich peaty soil. Drainage channels were dug, and at first water flowed by gravity out to the rivers and the sea. However, as the peat became exposed to the air, it shrank as it dried and decomposed. As a result, the land dropped by as much as four metres and became even more vulnerable to catastrophic flooding. Today, much of the drained fenland is close to sea level. The result was a curious upside-down landscape, where the waterways were now higher than the surrounding land. So water had to be pumped up into the drainage channels, first by wind pumps and then by steam and diesel engines. By the eighteenth and nineteenth centuries, the reclaimed land at last became better protected from frequent floods, providing rich pasture for sheep and cattle, and opportunities for intensive arable farming, with wheat, potatoes and other crops grown in the fertile black soil.

As the land was drained, the remains of the ancient forests, from pre-fenland times, became exposed in the peat. Known locally as 'bog oaks', these are several species including yew, pine and oak. Some trunks are 20 metres long and a metre thick and have been dated at over 5,000 years old. By the end of the nineteenth century, more than 99 per cent of the old fens had gone. Today the wildlife has retreated to the few remaining fragments of wetland on the edge of the old fenland basin, which has become a vast sea of agricultural land, devoted to human consumption. For reed warblers or cuckoos now arriving in the spring, Wicken Fen must appear as a tiny oasis in a desert.

Wicken Sedge Fen escaped being drained because of its easy accessibility to the local villagers, who fiercely guarded their rights to come here to cut sedge and peat. An old map by Theophilus Byrd, dating from 1666, shows how the fen was divided among the commoners. The path from the village to these plots through the middle of the fen, 'Sedge Fen Drove', has been kept clear by mowing since the seventeenth century. Every time I walk along this drove, where I have numbered tags along the ditches on either side, I am reminded that I am not the first to mark out a territory here.

Wicken Fen has been owned and managed by the National Trust since 1899. Most of the reserve was acquired, piece by piece, during the first decades of the twentieth century. As peat was replaced as a source of fuel by coal, and sedge was replaced for roofing by tiles, there were concerns that the sedge fen might suffer the same fate as the surrounding land and be drained for agriculture. By then it had become a famous hunting ground for Victorian entomologists and botanists. George Verrall (1848–1911) and Charles Rothschild (1877–1923), both Presidents of the Royal Entomological Society, were among the pioneers of conservation who had the foresight to buy parts of the fen to protect its habitat, and they bequeathed their plots of land to the National Trust. The fen had long been renowned for its rich wildlife. Seventy years earlier, when Charles Darwin was an undergraduate at Cambridge (from 1828 to 1831), he 'employed a labourer . . . to collect the rubbish at the bottom of the barges in which reeds are brought from the fens', and 'thus got some very rare species'. Darwin's teacher, John Stevens Henslow, also brought students to collect insects and plants on the edge of Wicken Fen.

The whole reserve, including the reclaimed agricultural land, is 750 hectares, and this includes just a tiny fragment, 169 hectares, of old undrained fen. Although it appears to be a wild place, it now has to be managed as intensively as the surrounding farmland. The main battle is to prevent the fen from drying out and turning itself into woodland scrub. This process of succession takes place naturally. It starts in open water where, as plants grow and die, their deposits become suitable for colonisation by reeds. The reed rhizomes spread through the mud, sending up shoots and slowly turning the habitat into a reed swamp. As the reeds die, the land then gradually rises and dries out. Sedge fields now take over, and as still more dead vegetation accumulates the land dries out further, becoming suitable for woodland, mainly buckthorn and alder buckthorn. What was once open water has become transformed over the years into dense scrub.

In the days of the old fens, this succession would have been prevented by frequent natural flooding. But now that the land surrounding Wicken Sedge Fen has been drained for agriculture, and protected from winter floods, there is a constant struggle to keep the fen wet by preventing water seeping out to the lower-lying farmland. Water has to be pumped into the fen, and sedge, reed and other grasses ('litter') have to be cropped periodically to prevent the accumulation of dead vegetation. Nevertheless, woodland scrub took over some drier areas during the early twentieth century and had to be cleared.

Large herbivores also now roam the fens once more, and the hope is that their trampling and grazing will help keep the habitat open and prevent the scrub from returning. As I look for nests in the reeds I am sometimes surprised by the sound of hooves galloping through the marsh, as Konik pony stallions herd their mares. This Polish breed has some characteristics of the extinct wild horses that graced Britain until 7,000 years ago, immortalised in old European cave paintings. They are short and stocky, with creamy-grey coats, and they look perfectly at home in the fen; their thick manes and long tails echo the seed heads of the old reeds blowing in the wind.

Highland cattle have been introduced, too. They spend long periods standing quietly, ruminating, and I've often emerged from the reeds to come face to face with a huge set of horns and a pair of small eyes staring blankly, as if in wonderment at what a human could find of interest there. They recall the aurochs, extinct wild cattle that used to roam the fens until 2,500 years ago. Aurochs bones are often found in fenland soils, including some skulls with Stone Age implements embedded in them, and a nearly complete skeleton unearthed near Wicken Fen.

When Nature managed the fens, there was plenty of suitable habitat for reed warblers and cuckoos. Now we are in charge, their future is in our hands. If we want reed warblers and cuckoos in our landscape we'll have to manage the land and pay for them, just as we do for our agricultural crops.

I climb the steps of the old Tower Hide, where there is a notice at the entrance: 'Please excuse the disgorged bones and mess; a barn owl sleeps here.' Built in 1956, the hide has a reed-thatched roof, with sedge-thatching along the ridge top, which is the traditional method in the fenland villages. For ridging, sedge is much more flexible and durable than reed. As I climb up inside the hide, I get glimpses of the fen through the wooden walls, which are drilled with woodpecker holes. Then, from the top, there is a bird's-eye view and I can survey my territory. I clear the owl pellets from the seat and then look out over a patchwork of habitats: a rich tapestry with a varied history since the days of the old fens.

Directly below me is a waterway, the Wicken Lode, some 10 metres wide and about a metre deep. Probably dating from

Roman times, this man-made canal ends at the edge of Wicken village, the entrance to the nature reserve. It winds westwards through the fen, meets two other lodes from the neighbouring villages of Burwell and Reach, and then flows northwest into the River Cam before joining the River Great Ouse and flowing out into the Wash and the North Sea. The lodes were constructed for transport between the villages, built on the higher ground and marooned as islands in the marshy land. The fens are also criss-crossed by smaller linear drainage channels. Around the edge of the fen are 'dykes', with gentle water flow. Then there are smaller 'drains', and even smaller 'ditches' which rarely flow and sometimes dry out altogether. The reeds fringing this network of lodes, dykes, drains and ditches will be home during the summer months for my reed warblers and cuckoos.

North towards the horizon is the eleventh-century cathedral of Ely, which sits on the raised land of the Isle of Ely, from where Hereward led his raids against the Normans. In the early mornings, when the mist lies low, the cathedral appears as a great ship, sailing across the fens. Below me, to the north of the lode, I look out over Wicken Sedge Fen, the small area that has never been drained and includes sedge fields and meadows, with grasses and wild flowers, divided by mown paths ('droves') and reed-fringed ditches.

To the south of the lode, the land has a different mood. It has been drained periodically and cultivated during the last 400 years and now lies a couple of metres lower than the level of the water in the lode. This is Adventurers' Fen, named after the speculators who invested in the great drainage schemes of the seventeenth century. One of my heroes, the artist Eric Ennion (1900–1981), wrote lyrically about his days in the village of Burwell, on the southern edge of Adventurers' Fen. During the agricultural depression in the 1920s and 1930s, the drainage system fell into disrepair and nature reclaimed the fen as it became flooded once more. In his book from 1942, *Adventurers Fen*, Ennion recalls the seasonal rhythm. Spring was the time for cutting the peat turf and stacking it to dry before it was loaded onto barges for transport. Summer was when the sedge and grasses were harvested. Then, in winter, the reeds were cut after the frost and wind had stripped the leaves. Winter was also the season for pollarding the willows to make wicker baskets and eel traps, and for punting along the drains and dykes to hunt wildfowl.

Eric Ennion trained as a doctor. In 1926 he joined his father's medical practice in Burwell, taking this over when his father died two years later and working there for 20 years. The duties of a night doctor in the fens could be an adventure in themselves:

> It was eerie at night to walk perhaps for miles along those narrow, slippery bank tops to some isolated farm or fenman's cottage. Sometimes a guide would meet me at a prearranged spot and walk ahead with a lantern.

His passions from an early age were birds and art. On Sundays, his one day off in the week, he'd be up at dawn with his sketch-book, to lose himself in his beloved fen. 'Spend Sunday as you will,' he wrote, 'to me, the race of the clouds across the sky, the ripple of wind on reeds and water, the cry of the birds, and a wealth of exercise, are hymn and psalm and sermon.' In case of medical emergencies that day he arranged a bush telegraph service: 'This entailed my wife with a flag nailed to a tall pole, a big tea tray and big gong stick to bang it with.' Whenever he heard the ominous banging on the tray, he'd pack up his sketch-book and run back to duty.

Ennion revolutionised how birds are depicted. He had no formal artistic training and developed his own style from watching for long hours in the field to get to know a bird's behaviour. Then he used his amazing visual memory to draw quickly and capture a moment on a page. His birds are not carefully posed to illustrate every plumage detail; they are impressions rather than portraits, wild and free. With a few deft strokes of his pencil, he captures their 'jizz'. A redshank, the watcher of the marsh, sleek and alert, ready to take flight and sound the alarm with its loud call. A heron poised to strike, its neck stretched and its eyes intent on the water below. A sparrowhawk braking with its tail outspread, talons thrust forward to snatch a young starling. He often included the bird's shadow, an essential part of a fleeting moment. Looking at his sketches, you can almost feel what it must be like to be a reed warbler; clasping a reed in both feet and being blown by a gust of wind. His art has taught me to look at birds in a fresh way, and has stimulated my appreciation of them as much as new scientific theories.

In 1941, Adventurers' Fen was drained once more and the reeds, sedge fields and sallows were burned to create agricultural land and provide food for Britain's hungry population during the war. 'Adventurers' Fen, in all its loveliness has gone,' Ennion lamented, and soon afterwards he gave up his medical practice and left to pioneer a Field Studies Centre at Flatford Mill in Suffolk. However, Adventurers' Fen has now become part of the Wicken Fen Reserve, managed by the National Trust, and the mosaic of reed beds and marsh land is slowly returning. One day, we may again be able to experience the former glory that inspired Eric Ennion more than 70 years ago.

At dusk, I climb down the steps of the Tower Hide and make my way home. With all my tags in place, my study site is marked out for the season, and I now await the arrival of the reed warblers and cuckoos. The barn owl is already out hunting, low and ghostly over the Sedge Fen. He has a favourite beat along the ditches and droves, flapping slowly and steadily into the wind on silent wings. Then he pauses, hovers briefly with talons outstretched, and drops to the ground. Perhaps he's caught a vole. Later tonight, back on his perch in the top deck of the hide, he'll regurgitate the fur and bones. There will be a fresh pile of pellets waiting on the seat for my next visit.

4

Harbinger of spring

A male reed warbler and a male cuckoo, both recently arrived from Africa. 19 May 2014.

A week later, the last days of April. The wind has changed to the south and the migrants are now pouring in. The fen is transformed. The reeds, so silent last visit, are suddenly alive with the '*chirps*' and '*chir-ups*' of male reed warblers, singing their jaunty, scratchy songs to set up their territories and attract mates. And then, in the distance, I hear my first '*cuck-oo*' of the year.

I catch a glimpse of him on the top of a tall ash tree, but he spots me first and flies off fast to the other side of the fen. Cuckoos are solitary and shy, more often heard than seen. William Wordsworth captures their elusiveness in his poem 'To the Cuckoo':

> O blithe New-comer! I have heard,
> I hear thee and rejoice.
> Oh Cuckoo! Shall I call thee Bird,
> Or but a wandering Voice?

In his book *Say Goodbye to the Cuckoo*, a lyrical celebration of our spring migrants and lament for their decline, Michael McCarthy comments:

> There was nothing in nature like the wandering voice. When it was paired . . . with the most eagerly awaited change of the turning year, the coming of spring, it is not an exaggeration to say that in Europe it became one of the

> most significant and resonant sounds in human life . . . The nightingale may have prompted more poetry; the cuckoo has prompted more proverbs.

In some regions, it was thought unlucky to hear a cuckoo before breakfast, while hearing the first cuckoo from one's bed was a sign of impending illness or death (enticements to get up early!). However, good fortune would come if a cuckoo was heard while out walking, and a child born on the first day a cuckoo calls in spring would be lucky all its life. The number of calls was also said to predict how long you had to live, your number of children, and so on. In Danish folklore, the cuckoo is said to be so busy with these forecasts that it has no time to build a nest!

Reed warblers and cuckoos continue to arrive on the fen throughout late April and May. Cuckoos are hard to watch, but most days I see two or three males chasing and '*cuck-ooing*'. They are similar in size to a collared dove, but the cuckoo's long pointed wings, long tail and barring underneath give it the appearance in flight of a bird of prey. When the male perches on a treetop to call, he adopts a characteristic posture, with his tail raised and his wings drooping below his body. Only the male calls '*cuck-oo*'; the female has a strange bubbling cry, a rapid series of 10–15 chuckle notes that fade towards the end. Females are shyer and rarely perch out in the open. On Wicken Fen, most females have a similar plumage to the males, ashy-grey above and white below, with brownish-black bars on the belly, but they are distinguishable if you get close, because they have some buff on the breast.

A few females are strikingly different in appearance, bright rufous above, barred with black.

As I become immersed in recording the breeding activities of the reed warblers, I know that the female cuckoos are watching them too, from their secret vantage posts. Female cuckoos search alone for host nests, unaccompanied by a male, and males are also not present when a female lays her egg, as if they know they'd only get in the way. Whenever I flush a female cuckoo from the bushes alongside the ditches, I suspect she curses me for interrupting her surveillance. However, many times I must walk past and be unaware of her presence. Once I saw a female land in a bush alongside a busy path, and during the next hour dozens of people walked within a few metres of her. She sat motionless and undetected, her grey upperparts and barred underparts a perfect camouflage against the branches.

Along some of the stretches, I mark the reed warblers with coloured rings so I can recognise them all individually. I catch them in mist nets, fine-meshed nets strung between vertical poles. The best time is early morning, before the sun rises and makes the nets more visible, and before the wind gets up and billows them, making them less effective. Most birds are easy to catch as they flit across gaps in the reeds or fly to feed in bushes nearby. But each year a few evade capture, probably because they hit the net, bounce out and then become more alert to the sight of the mesh. Then I have to try various tricks, including new netting sites or the gentle art of 'pishing'.

It's not known why 'pishing' can be so effective. You make a loud '*pish, pish*' sound by blowing gently through the lips. Often a reed warbler will immediately approach and climb up the reeds to see what's going on. Sometimes, by pishing on the other side of the net, I can lure the birds to fly in and get caught. Once, with a really tricky individual, I lay on the ground directly under the net and pished as loudly as I could. The bird flew straight towards me, hit the soft mesh and hung there, just a few centimetres from my face.

It's always a thrill to hold a reed warbler gently in your hand, especially a new arrival in spring that has dropped from the night skies a few hours before. The journey this little bird has made is truly astonishing. Just 11 or 12 grams in weight, less than a large envelope, it has flown here from its wintering grounds in West Africa, a distance of some 4,300 kilometres. Travelling by night, with stopovers to fatten up and fuel each stage of the journey, it has crossed the Sahara, the Mediterranean, Spain, France, the English Channel, and then southern England, a trip likely to have taken several weeks. Now its home for three months will be a 20-metre stretch of reeds. I place a numbered metal ring on one leg and then two colour rings on the other leg, a unique combination that will enable me to recognise it individually. As I release it, I wonder if this will be one that gets tricked by a cuckoo, and doomed to spend the summer raising a chick of the wrong species.

I follow the activities of my reed warblers daily over the coming weeks. Once they are colour-ringed, I get to know them as individuals and really do feel they are 'mine' in the sense that I want to follow their progress through the season, rather like keeping in touch with old friends. I also wonder how the female cuckoo might keep track of her hosts. What cues could she use to find a host nest and time the laying of her egg to coincide with the reed warbler's own egg-laying period? This is what I see, and what the female cuckoo must be observing carefully.

Male reed warblers arrive first and set up a territory. Along the lodes and ditches, each male occupies a linear stretch of about 20 metres of reeds, which he proclaims by song and defends throughout the summer. Along wider waterways just one bank is defended, but in the narrow ditches males defend both banks. Unpaired males sing for most of the day. When the poet John Clare heard a nightingale singing in an apple tree in May 1832, he could transcribe the song ('take down her notes') as a poem of 22 short lines because, although the nightingale repeats notes, it pauses between phrases. The reed warbler, by contrast, pours out its song as a continuous flow of repeated notes, often for 30 seconds and sometimes for several minutes, so the transcription should read as one uninterrupted line:

> cheu-cheu-cheu, trp-trp, chuck-chuck, kek-kek-kek, tui-tui-tui, whit-chuck, whit-chuck, whit-chuck, trup-trup, werchee-werchee, whit-whit-chu, ptcherr-ptcherr, chirr-chirr-chirr, chirruc-chirruc . . .

When the females begin to arrive, about a week later, pairs form quickly. It's easy to tell when a male has attracted a mate: he sings much less and switches to shorter songs, as a 'keep out' signal to rivals. As I walk along the reed fringes, I often hear newly formed pairs chatting to each other with soft '*chup*' calls.

As soon as reed warbler pairs form, nest building begins within a day or two. Only the female builds the nest, and the male often follows her, back and forth, while she collects material. Early nests are built low down, often just half a metre above the water surface and in old reeds, the only source of cover at the start of the season. But new reeds are preferred, and once they grow, and their fresh green leaves can conceal a nest from above, nests are built higher, a metre or more above the water. Low nests are vulnerable to attack from below by moorhens, which swim by and pull the nests down to eat the eggs. This probably explains the reed warblers' preference for higher sites, but only when cover is available, because there are also predators searching from above. Jays will fly down from nearby trees to take eggs or chicks. Sitting adult reed warblers might also be snatched by the talons of a marsh harrier sailing overhead.

Almost all the nests are built over water, which helps to provide protection from ground predators, particularly weasels. When a ditch dried out one summer, I watched a weasel approach a nest with young chicks, no doubt attracted by their loud begging cries. The weasel climbed to the nest in a flash, and by the time I'd rushed up to check it had run off with one chick, and the three remaining chicks lay dead in the nest, each with a bite mark in the skull. A season's hard work was over in a moment. The weasel later returned for the rest of the brood.

The nests are woven around reed stems, usually from three to seven (the average is four). More supports are used where the reeds are denser. Among sparser reeds, where nests are built around just two or three stems, they are more likely to slip or become torn from their attachments by the storms that sweep across the fen. So the female's choice of nest site is important. Older males, who have bred on the fen in previous years, arrive about a week earlier than young males born the year before, and they tend to pair up first, perhaps partly because they claim the best nest sites. Males in poorer sites sing for two or three weeks before they attract a mate. By this time, other pairs might already have young chicks. So the onset of egg laying varies between different waterways on the fen, depending on how soon the reeds have grown to provide cover. Staggered egg laying results in nests for cuckoos throughout the season and is no doubt one of the features that make reed warblers such attractive hosts.

The nest is a work of art, a deep cup built of strips torn from reed stems and leaves. The cup and attachments to the reed stems are strengthened with spider silk. One of the most magical moments of the summer is to watch a female reed warbler, backlit by the rising sun, collecting shining threads from the webs strung between the reed tops. I find some nests by watching females building, but the best method is simply to walk along the banks and part the reeds every few metres with a stick.

My stick becomes my trusty companion throughout the summer, as essential for fieldwork as binoculars and notebook. Each one lasts three or four seasons until it is broken by accident, usually when I'm clumsy and lean on it too hard while climbing out of a ditch. Then I feel a sense of loss until a good replacement is found. The ideal stick is shoulder height, about the thickness of my thumb, with a curve towards the end for holding the reeds apart. I become familiar with the feel and weight of it, as a fisherman might become attached to a favourite rod, and I enjoy the rhythm of sweeping through the reeds, searching among the forest of stems and leaves. It's easiest to find nests looking into the sunlight, when their silhouettes are visible. With the sun behind, the strong reflection of light from the reeds makes the nests hard to see.

The nest cup is completed in four or five days. Then it is lined with finer material, hair and the thin fibres from old reed seeds. Once the lining is complete, egg laying usually begins two to four days later. This must be when a female cuckoo needs to watch most closely, so she can time her parasitic laying correctly. However, during the period between finishing the nest and the start of egg laying, reed warblers become much harder to observe. Sometimes the female leaves her territory to feed in bushes nearby, which are undefended areas where she is more likely to encounter other reed warblers.

Wherever she goes, inside the territory or beyond, her male follows closely, within a metre or two. He is guarding her from the advances of other males, because this is the time that she is fertile and begins to solicit copulations. If the male fails to see his female fly off, he sings intensively in the reeds or searches through the territory until he finds her. My observations of colour-ringed individuals show that during his female's fertile period, a male has to chase off male intruders once or twice an hour. Intruders are secretive; most come from the nearest neighbouring territories, but some come from as far as four territories away. These intruders are usually males who are not busy guarding their own females, either because their females have not yet begun to build a nest or because their clutches are complete. So the intruders are free to roam without risking lost paternity back home.

During this mate-guarding period, the females of some species of birds try to escape the close attentions of their mates in order to solicit copulations from other males, and they sometimes fly across several territory boundaries to do so. Careful studies of several species have revealed that a male's display is a signal of his genetic quality; males with more elaborate displays tend to survive better, and they pass on their genetic superiority to their offspring. In support of the idea that females are shopping for good genes for their offspring, females target particularly attractive males for these flings away from home, or 'extra-pair' copulations, as they are technically called. What is deemed attractive by females varies between species. For some species it is the complexity of a male's song; for others it is the brightness of his plumage. Females tend to choose extra-pair copulations from males whose songs are more complex, or whose plumage is brighter, than that of their own males. Females already paired to attractive males, according to these features, are more faithful.

Female birds have sperm stores, little blind-ending tubules in their reproductive tract where they can store viable sperm for a week or more. So if a female copulates with more than one male, she will have a mix of sperm from rival males in her stores, and the result is often mixed paternity in the brood. In some species where females are particularly promiscuous, such as the reed bunting, half or more of the offspring are sired by extra-pair males.

Using DNA markers to assign paternity, we discovered that most female reed warblers on Wicken Fen are faithful to their mates. Only 15 per cent of broods contained young sired by extra-pair males, usually just one chick in a brood. In total, only 6 per cent of all the nestlings were sired by extra-pair copulations. Perhaps male reed warblers are able to guard their females closely. Or perhaps a female reed warbler usually rejects extra-pair suitors. Studies of other species have shown that if a male detects he has been 'cuckolded' then he might provide less help in raising the brood, for which he cannot be sure of full paternity. If a female reed warbler had to rely on her mate's hard work for the successful rearing of her young, then it might pay her to be faithful to be sure of his full parental effort.

Reed warblers lay their eggs soon after dawn, one per day and on successive days. Most clutches on Wicken Fen are of four eggs, sometimes three or five, and rarely two or six. Once the first egg is laid, males suddenly reduce their guarding of the female and spend more time near the nest. Why is this? Experiments with captive zebra finches, by Tim Birkhead and his colleagues at the University of Sheffield, have shown that extra-pair copulations are most potent prior to the onset of egg laying, but nevertheless they can still be a threat to the guarding male's paternity even after the first egg is laid. An egg is fertilised about 24 hours before it is laid. So once the first egg is laid, the second egg in the clutch, due to be laid the next day, will already have been fertilised. Provided the paired male has guarded his female successfully, therefore, he can be sure of paternity of the first two eggs. But the third and fourth eggs are still at risk of being fertilised by any subsequent extra-pair copulations. Why doesn't the male continue to guard until the third egg is laid, and hence his paternity of the final, fourth egg is secure?

There may be several reasons why a male reed warbler uses the laying of the first egg as a cue to stop mate guarding. First, studies of other species have shown that females are less likely to solicit copulations once the first egg is laid. Secondly, a male copulates with his mate several times a day for the week or so prior to the start of egg laying, so his sperm will usually be numerically dominant in her storage tubules by the time eggs are ready to be fertilised. So perhaps the appearance of the first egg is a signal that the male can relax. There may be another reason, too, for his sudden change in behaviour. With the laying of the first egg, the nest now becomes vulnerable to parasitism. Perhaps he should turn his attention from guarding against cuckoldry to guarding against cuckoos.

When the nest has just one or two eggs, the male spends most of his time close by, keeping watch, and occasionally he sits on the nest. When I check nests on these days, he often reacts to my presence with a few song phrases. Incubation, and hence egg development, usually begins in earnest with the laying of the last (usually the fourth) egg. Male and female then take equal turns at sitting, alternating spells which vary from 10 to 30 minutes in length. Changeovers are rapid and take place with the minimum of fuss. The sitting bird slips away as its partner announces its imminent arrival with a soft '*chup*' call.

The chicks usually hatch after 12 days' incubation. Often the first two or three eggs hatch a day earlier than the last egg, because they had a head start in development when the male sat on them before the clutch was completed. As a result, there are often chicks of different sizes in the nest. The nestlings are then fed by both parents for about 10–12 days. They leave the nest before their wings are full grown, clambering among the reeds like little acrobats, and clinging on with their strong feet. At first they sit quietly, waiting for their parents to come and feed them. So still are they at this stage, and so well camouflaged, with their warm brown plumage a good match for the old reeds, that I have often parted the reeds, when searching for nests, and found a little fledgling perched just a few centimetres from my nose.

As they get older, the young begin to follow their parents around the territory and in excursions to the bushes on the bank. By 10–14 days after leaving the nest, their wing and tail feathers are more or less fully grown, so they are adept at catching their own food. They then become independent of their parents and leave the natal territory. Pairs who have a successful brood early in the season may have time to build another nest and raise a second brood. But most pairs raise just one. Many lose their eggs or nestlings to predators, such as jays. Once this occurs, within a day or two the female begins to build a replacement nest in a new site in the territory, often using the old nest material for the new nest.

Over the last 30 years, I have never ceased to be amazed at the energy that parent reed warblers devote to these breeding activities: the male's setting up of his territory, his continuous singing to attract a mate, his guarding of the female while she builds and is fertile, the sharing of incubation and chick-feeding duties, and the speed with which they start all over again if the nest is lost at any of these stages. How truly remarkable it is, then, that the cuckoo can infiltrate this routine. Surely, we may suppose, reed warblers must take the same degree of care in their defences against cuckoo parasitism.

During my first three summers' fieldwork on Wicken Fen in the 1980s, I teamed up with my good friend from student days, Michael Brooke, now Curator of Birds at the Museum of Zoology in Cambridge, and we monitored all the reed warbler nests we could find to determine how many got parasitised by cuckoos. We divided the fen into two halves. That we should each have our own territory seemed entirely natural and appealed to our hunting instincts. In fact we had fun trying to beat each other in the number of nests or cuckoo eggs we found. This arrangement has always taken place whenever I have subsequently worked with a male colleague. Neither of us would dream of trespassing onto the other's territory without permission. If we did so, we'd have felt as guilty as an intruding reed warbler.

My female colleagues find this way of doing fieldwork very odd. They usually prefer to cover the whole area together, as a shared territory. And they have just as much fun cooperating, and find just as many nests as Mike and I ever did. Nevertheless, my territorial instinct remains strong, even after nearly 30 years on Wicken Fen. Recently, the fen wardens told me that a visitor had reported seeing an old man with a stick, searching for nests along my stretches of reeds. I had a restless night wondering if an egg collector might be at work. When I awoke the next morning, my mind clear, I relaxed as I realised suddenly that the old man must have been me!

During the first two years of our study, 1985 and 1986, Mike and I monitored a total of 274 reed warbler nests daily during egg laying. Of these, 44 (16 per cent) were parasitised by cuckoos; 38 of the nests had just a single cuckoo egg, but six had two cuckoo eggs. Just as Edgar Chance did, we could recognise individual female cuckoos' eggs by variation in their ground colour and markings. In all six nests with two cuckoo eggs, it was clear from their different colour and markings that these were laid by two different female cuckoos.

Like Chance's cuckoos, many of our females laid eggs in distinct territories. For example, I found seven eggs from one female all along the same ditch, a stretch of 400 metres, and seven from another female along another ditch, 850 metres long. Each of these females had about 20 reed warbler nests in her egg-laying territory, so clearly she didn't parasitise every one.

I experienced some of Chance's excitement from 60 years earlier, trying to predict which nests my cuckoos would choose. I didn't always get it right! On one afternoon I was expecting a female to lay an egg, as she had laid an egg two days before. There were two suitable reed warbler nests in her territory, where the clutch had been started but was not yet complete. One of the nests was right by the Visitor Centre, where there was a party of schoolchildren and wardens working with tractors. The other was in a quiet part of the fen, so that's where I took up my position to wait, hoping to witness the laying. There was no sign of the cuckoo and then, soon after 5 p.m., to my surprise I heard a female's bubble cry from the direction of the Visitor Centre. I checked the nest there, and sure enough she'd just laid her egg. There were some 30 people nearby. Not one of them had seen her.

Coloured rings are a good method for following individual reed warblers, but cuckoos are so shy and difficult to observe that the only sure way to study their movements is by radio-tracking. A small transmitter is glued to the feathers on the bird's back, and the signal can then be picked up with an antenna from up to three kilometres away. The transmitter usually lasts for a couple of months, which is long enough to follow a cuckoo for a whole breeding season. At the end of the summer, when the bird moults, it falls off.

The first study was carried out in the 1970s by Ian Wyllie, who radio-tracked cuckoos on the edge of the fens, near St Ives, Cambridgeshire. He recognised other cuckoos individually by marking them with coloured wing tags. His cuckoos targeted reed warblers as hosts, just as on Wicken Fen. Each male cuckoo had a singing area of about 30 hectares (one hectare is 100 × 100 metres) which overlapped the singing areas of up to four other males. So the males clearly did not defend exclusive territories.

Each female laid her eggs in a distinct area, also about 30 hectares. For some females, this was indeed an exclusive territory. However, sometimes a female shared her egg-laying area with up to three other females. When there was overlap, one female appeared to be dominant and laid more eggs than the others. The breeding area of one of the radio-tracked females was overlapped by six different males during the season, and sometimes several males were seen following her around at once.

Radio-tracking of cuckoos that parasitised reed warblers in Germany revealed similar patterns to Wyllie's study. Male cuckoos often had overlapping singing territories. Dominant females defended egg-laying territories, to which they returned in successive years. Subordinate females had ranges that overlapped the range of one or more dominant females, and they laid fewer eggs. They inherited the breeding territory when a dominant female disappeared.

These studies show that female cuckoos compete for areas with a good supply of host nests. Sometimes one female can defend her egg-laying area as an exclusive territory. It's not known how she does this. Perhaps her bubble cry serves as a 'keep out' signal to other females. However, if many females are attracted to the site, perhaps because there are many host nests, then subordinate or nomadic females might occasionally lay eggs in a dominant female's territory. This explains why we sometimes find two cuckoo eggs in the same nest.

At first, this competition for host nests seems odd, given that only a small proportion of nests are parasitised; just 16 per cent in our first two years on Wicken Fen, and less than 5 per cent of reed warbler nests over the whole of Britain. Surely there should be plenty of host nests to go round? However, not all reed warbler nests are accessible to cuckoos. Female cuckoos look for nests by watching the hosts from concealed perches in bushes and trees. On Wicken Fen, we found that the probability of parasitism declines dramatically with increasing distance from a suitable cuckoo lookout perch: from 22 per cent parasitism for nests within five metres of a lookout perch, to 10 per cent for nests 10 metres away, 5 per cent for nests 20 metres away and less than 1 per cent for nests further than 40 metres. So there is competition for those accessible nests that are within the range of cuckoo detection.

Male cuckoos play no part in egg laying; their success depends simply on the number of females they can mate with and their ability to keep other males at bay, to ensure their paternity. So while female cuckoos focus on hosts, male cuckoos focus on female cuckoos. Sometimes a male may be able to monopolise a female's breeding range and gain exclusive access to her. For example, a female cuckoo studied by Mike Bayliss in an isolated Oxfordshire reed bed laid nine eggs in reed warbler nests one summer, and DNA profiles from her chicks confirmed that they were all sired by the same male.

However, when host densities are high and many female cuckoos are attracted to the same site, there may be many male cuckoos with overlapping ranges, all competing for mating opportunities. Hiroshi Nakamura, from Shinshu University in Japan, studied a high-density site in the suburbs of Nagano City, where common cuckoos were parasitising great reed warblers that nested in the reed beds along the Chikuma River. He followed the cuckoos both by radio-tracking and by marking them with coloured wing tags and found that several males and females shared the same range. So both male and female cuckoos had access to many potential mates. DNA profiles of the cuckoo chicks at this study site revealed that many of the females had offspring sired by two or three different males during the same season, and many males sired offspring with up to four females.

Radio-tracking studies also reveal an unusual pattern to cuckoo movements, which makes it more difficult for a female cuckoo to secure exclusive access to her host nests, and more difficult, too, for a male cuckoo to guard a female cuckoo. Both male and female cuckoos may feed a long way from the breeding areas, often four or five kilometres away but sometimes as far as 23 kilometres. These sites are usually orchards or patches of woodland rich in hairy caterpillars, the cuckoo's favourite prey. Cuckoos do not call in these feeding areas; all the calling takes place back at the breeding site. Hiroshi Nakamura's observations showed that, on average, cuckoos spent only half their time each day in the breeding areas. Males tended to arrive at dawn and then left for their feeding areas in the late morning, sometimes returning for an hour or two in the early evening. Females arrived at the breeding site later and were more likely to stay on into the afternoon, especially on egg-laying days.

It was with great excitement that Mike Brooke and I checked our reed warbler nests on Wicken Fen each day. Would there be a cuckoo egg in the clutch? Would the reed warblers accept it? I can still remember the thrill of discovering my first cuckoo egg. There were three reed warbler eggs in the nest at midday; then, when I checked again at 6 p.m. one of the eggs had gone and had been replaced by a cuckoo egg. The cuckoo egg was obvious because it was a little larger than the two remaining reed warbler eggs, and also rounder in shape. Furthermore, although the background matched the greenish background of the reed warbler eggs, the cuckoo's egg had finer speckling. My first thought was: if it's obvious to me, why isn't it also obvious to the reed warblers? So I sat on the bank to watch the nest through a small gap in the reeds.

The male returned to the nest within a minute. He perched on the rim and looked intently at the clutch. Then he spent a minute or so poking into the bottom of the nest with his bill. Apparently satisfied all was well, he then settled down to incubate, shuffling low so just his bill tip and eye showed above the rim on one side, with his tail sticking up on the other side. After 20 minutes, he left suddenly without a sound and within a few seconds the female arrived. She perched on the nest rim and poked about in the nest, intent on inspecting the clutch. But then she, too, settled down to incubate. I left my watch, puzzled that neither of the pair seemed to have noticed the foreign egg.

I inspected the nest again the following afternoon. The female had laid another egg, so there were now three reed warbler eggs in the nest. But the cuckoo egg had gone. So within a day the warblers had rejected it. In total, out of the 44 parasitised clutches Mike and I found in 1985 and 1986, two clutches were destroyed by predators soon after the cuckoo egg was laid, so we were not able to determine the warblers' response. At eight of the remaining 42 nests the reed warblers rejected the cuckoo egg. In four cases, the cuckoo egg was ejected from the nest. We found one of the ejected cuckoo eggs, still whole, under the nest at the bottom of the ditch below a metre of water. In the other four cases, the warblers deserted the clutch and the female immediately began to dismantle the nest, using the material to build a new nest nearby. So at 19 per cent of the nests the cuckoo egg was rejected and at 81 per cent it was accepted. We found that there was often a day or two before the hosts rejected the cuckoo egg. This delay means that it is unlikely that we missed some ejections simply because they occurred so soon after the cuckoo egg was laid that we failed to record the nest as parasitised.

Mike and I were thrilled to find that reed warblers were not always duped. The advantage to them of spotting a cuckoo egg is obvious. On Wicken Fen, it takes about 47 days to raise an average brood of four reed warbler young: six days to build the nest, four days to lay the eggs (one per day), 12 days to incubate the clutch, 11 days to feed the nestlings, and 14 days to feed the fledglings until independence. Most pairs will have time for just one successful brood per season, while those that start early might just squeeze in two broods. A cuckoo chick, however, takes about two weeks longer to rear (19 days as a nestling, two to three weeks as a fledgling). So an unlucky pair of reed warblers, parasitised in their first nest, would take so long to raise the cuckoo chick that there would be no time to raise any of their own young that year. For hosts, a cuckoo egg in the nest is potentially more disastrous than having all their eggs or chicks taken by a predator. Accepting a cuckoo dooms them to no reproductive success that summer, while after predation at least there's a chance to try again.

Now consider the savings from rejecting a cuckoo egg. If the reed warblers eject the cuckoo egg, then they save the remainder of their clutch, so all they have lost is the egg that the female cuckoo removed when she parasitised the nest. From their initial clutch of four eggs, therefore, reed warblers that eject a cuckoo egg have the chance to raise three of their own chicks, just one fewer than those that had escaped parasitism in the first place. Even if the reed warblers respond by deserting the clutch, perhaps because they are unable to eject the cuckoo egg, they still make a considerable saving. They can now immediately begin a new nest and have another opportunity to raise a brood of their own.

So the cuckoos don't always win. What cues do the warblers use to detect a cuckoo egg? What are the cuckoo's tricks to beat host defences? Mike and I decided to investigate these questions by experiments in the field, and we realised that the best way to do this would be to become cuckoos ourselves.

5

Playing cuckoo

A female reed warbler collecting spider silk for her nest, with her mate close by, under the watchful eye of a female cuckoo.
Wicken Fen, 20 May 2014.

I have a recipe for making cuckoo eggs. I borrow a cuckoo egg from a museum; make a mould around it, in two halves; pour resin into the two halves, stick them together and wait for it to harden; open the two halves of the mould – and there is a model cuckoo egg, of exactly the same dimensions and weight as a real cuckoo egg. With acrylic paints, I now paint them various colours to represent the different races of cuckoo: green and speckled for reed warbler specialist cuckoos, brown and speckled for meadow pipit specialist cuckoos, greyish-white and speckled for pied wagtail specialist cuckoos, and immaculate plain blue for redstart specialist cuckoos. I have a hundred of these model cuckoo eggs on my desk. Now I'm ready to become a cuckoo myself.

Let's go back to consider the cuckoo's egg-laying procedure, so beautifully revealed by Edgar Chance. First of all, we might ask questions about the cuckoo egg itself. Why do the various races of cuckoo lay 'mimetic' eggs, namely eggs which match the appearance of the eggs of their different host species? Why is the cuckoo egg so small? It is similar in size to the host's eggs, but to achieve this, the common cuckoo lays a remarkably small egg for a bird of its size.

Then we might ask questions about the egg-laying procedure. Why does the female cuckoo wait until the hosts have begun their clutch before she parasitises the nest? Why does she remove a host egg before she lays her own? Why is her laying visit so incredibly quick?

Finally, we can wonder about the cuckoo chick. Why does it eject the host eggs and young? Why is the ejecting the job of the newly hatched cuckoo chick? Surely it would be easier for the mother cuckoo to do the work beforehand, by removing all the host eggs before she parasitises the nest with her egg.

The obvious answer to all these questions is that the cuckoo's tactics are designed to beat host defences. If the cuckoo did not lay a mimetic egg, one similar in size and appearance to the host's own eggs, if she was slower or made a mistake with her timing, if she failed to remove a host egg, and so on, then the hosts would be more likely to detect that they had been parasitised, and to reject the cuckoo egg. With a batch of model cuckoo eggs at the ready, and a licence to permit our research, we can test all these conjectures experimentally, by playing the part of the cuckoo ourselves. Our idea was to vary each part of the cuckoo's egg-laying procedure in turn, to see whether it helped to deceive the reed warblers and, if so, how.

The first thing Mike Brooke and I discovered is that being a cuckoo is hard work! To do our experiments, we had to find lots of reed warbler nests, and at the right stage, namely during the egg-laying period. Nevertheless, it was great fun to put a model egg into a nest and then return at daily intervals to see whether the reed warblers had accepted it. The model eggs looked realistic to our eyes and they warmed up when the warblers sat on them, just like real eggs. We were delighted when our friend Bruce Campbell, one of Britain's most experienced ornithologists at the time, came across one of our experimental nests and noted it as parasitised by a real cuckoo.

First, we tested whether it was important for the cuckoo egg to match the host egg in colour and spotting. Stuart Baker, in 1913, was the first to suggest that discrimination by hosts selected for egg mimicry by cuckoos:

> The process of perfect adaptation is attained by the slow but sure elimination by the foster parents of those eggs which contrast most distinctively with their own . . . by this means those strains of cuckoos which lay the most ill-adapted eggs gradually die out, whilst those that lay eggs most like those of the fosterer are enabled to persist.

Baker found tantalising evidence for host discrimination from his studies of the common cuckoo in India. He compared the fates of occasional badly matching cuckoo eggs, apparently laid by a different race of cuckoo, with those of well-matching eggs, laid by the race that normally specialised on a particular host species. In total, he found that 12 out of 21 badly matching cuckoo eggs were deserted (57 per cent) compared with only six out of 158 well-matching eggs (4 per cent). These results certainly suggest that hosts might be particular about egg appearance. However, perhaps other factors caused the greater desertion of badly matching eggs. For example, a foreign race of cuckoo might have taken longer to find the nest of an unfamiliar host species. This might have caused increased disturbance and have led to greater host desertion. To be sure that egg appearance itself influences host rejection, we need to do an experiment in which we vary egg appearance while keeping everything else constant.

Our experiments showed that reed warblers were, indeed, particular about the appearance of the eggs in their nest. They accepted almost all the model eggs that we painted to resemble their own eggs in colour and spotting (green, just like those laid by the race of cuckoo that specialises on reed warblers). However, they rejected two-thirds of the model eggs that clearly differed from their own, for example brown, spotted eggs typical of the cuckoo race that specialises on meadow pipits, greyish-white and speckled eggs of the cuckoo race that specialises on pied wagtails, or immaculate blue eggs of the cuckoo race specialising on redstarts. The rejections occurred in exactly the same manner as for real cuckoo eggs; in about half the cases the model egg was ejected from the nest (we found some of these in the water below) and in half the clutch was deserted, often following a bout of pecking at the model egg.

Just as with real cuckoo eggs, the reed warblers usually waited until they had completed their clutch before they rejected a model egg. The first time I placed a blue cuckoo egg into a reed warbler nest, I sat on the bank to watch, expecting the warblers to eject it straight away. When they accepted it throughout that day, I went home wondering if the model egg experiments would fail altogether. Perhaps, I thought, the warblers realised our eggs were fake and accepted them as harmless inanimate objects. But the subsequent responses, once the clutch was completed, showed clearly that acceptance depended on the appearance of the foreign egg, not the fact that it was made of resin. The moral is: always have controls for every experiment (in this case, eggs that matched the warblers' own eggs) and be patient! We wondered if the delay in rejection was because it was easier to spot an odd egg once the whole clutch was there for comparison.

Male and female reed warblers share incubation, and it was clear from watching their pecking at the models that both rejected eggs unlike their own. However, the pair did not always agree. At one nest, the male continued to incubate a clutch with a badly matching model egg, while the female slowly dismantled the nest beneath him, using the material to build a new nest nearby. This was amusing to watch; every time the female pulled out a beakful of material, the male peered over the nest rim, as if wondering what was going on. After several hours, with the nest now almost completely taken away, the male was forced to agree to the move.

Whenever the warblers deserted, either in response to one of our model eggs or in response to a real cuckoo egg, they usually built a new nest nearby, but sometimes they built their new nest over the top of the old one. The result was a deep, two-storey nest with the old, deserted clutch buried on the bottom floor and the replacement clutch above. Why do this rather than build at a new site? Perhaps this reduces the chance of being parasitised again. If female cuckoos remember the sites where they have already laid, and leave these nests free from further interference, then it would pay the warblers to build their new nest on top of the old one. The female cuckoo might then be fooled into regarding this as the same nest she had already parasitised and so would leave it alone. Perhaps a nest in a new site would be more readily noticed as a new nest? It would be fun to test this idea one day.

Our discovery that reed warblers were more likely to accept a cuckoo egg of similar appearance to their own eggs may seem such an obvious and expected result that one might wonder if the experiment was worth doing. However, there are at least two alternative hypotheses for why cuckoos might evolve mimetic eggs. Alfred Russel Wallace, Darwin's contemporary, and co-discoverer of the principle of natural selection, was fascinated by camouflage and thought that birds' eggs were a fine example of protective colouration. If it was important for host eggs to be camouflaged to decrease predation, then surely this would apply to cuckoo eggs too: 'If each bird's eggs are to some extent protected by their harmony of colour with their surroundings,' he wrote in 1889, 'the presence of a larger and very differently coloured egg in the nest might be dangerous and lead to the destruction of the whole set.' Wallace's idea was that host and cuckoo eggs had independently evolved the same colours and patterns so that the clutch was not made conspicuous to predators. Therefore, even in the absence of any host discrimination, cuckoo egg mimicry could still evolve through selective predation.

We were able to test Wallace's hypothesis by following the success of the reed warbler nests in which we placed model eggs. However, our results did not support his idea: there was no tendency for predators to take more of the clutches with a non-mimetic cuckoo egg than those with a mimetic cuckoo egg.

The third hypothesis for the evolution of egg mimicry comes from the observation that sometimes a female cuckoo lays in a nest that has already been parasitised by another cuckoo, a consequence of the overlapping ranges of some female cuckoos. Now there is only room for one young cuckoo per nest; if two hatch out, then there is a struggle in which one will eventually evict the other. This was first described in 1788 by Edward Jenner, who found two young cuckoos in a dunnock nest:

> Two cuckoos were hatched in the same nest this morning. In a few hours after, a contest began between the cuckoos for the possession of the nest, which continued undetermined till the next afternoon; when one of them, which was somewhat superior in size, turned out the other. This contest was very remarkable. The combatants alternately

> appeared to have the advantage, as each carried the other several times nearly to the top of the nest, and then sunk down again, oppressed by the weight of its burden; till at length, after various efforts, the strongest prevailed.

As Edgar Chance discovered, the female cuckoo first removes an egg before she lays her own. If the nest has already been parasitised, it would clearly pay the second cuckoo to pick out the first cuckoo's egg for removal, especially as that egg is likely to hatch out first and so her own chick is more likely to lose the battle for possession of the nest. In theory, then, host egg mimicry could evolve because a mimetic cuckoo egg is less likely to be recognised and removed by another female cuckoo which comes to lay an egg in the same nest.

We were able to test this hypothesis, too, because sometimes a cuckoo visited a nest in which we had placed a model egg. Surprisingly, we found that cuckoos were not more likely to remove a model egg if it differed in colour from the host eggs. Our observations of cuckoos laying in nests where there was already a real cuckoo egg also showed that cuckoos weren't selective when they removed an egg. They simply picked an egg at random. Therefore we found no evidence that egg mimicry might help to protect a cuckoo egg from removal by other cuckoos.

Mike and I are still puzzled by this result. Surely cuckoos should be on the lookout for other cuckoo eggs, and should remove them. Films of female cuckoos at host nests show that after the female has laid her egg she flies off immediately; she never looks back in the nest. So perhaps she never gets to know what a cuckoo egg looks like compared with host eggs. Nevertheless, surely any female cuckoo that removed the oddest or largest egg in the clutch before she laid her own would be at an advantage. Cuckoos take such care in parasitism that it is strange that they don't add this extra refinement to the laying procedure.

Nevertheless, even if cuckoos did come to discriminate, and they picked out odd-looking eggs for removal, their selective pressure would still be less strong than that from host discrimination. On Wicken Fen, only 14 per cent of parasitised nests were visited by a second cuckoo, whereas hosts rejected non-mimetic eggs at 69 per cent of host nests. In other words, a badly matching cuckoo egg has at most a 14 per cent chance of being removed by another cuckoo, compared with a 69 per cent chance of being removed by the reed warblers themselves.

These experiments show clearly that the cuckoo egg is more likely to deceive the hosts if it matches the host eggs in colour and spotting. What about egg size? Does that have to match too? Parasitic cuckoos lay remarkably small eggs, much smaller than those of non-parasitic cuckoos of the same body size. The egg of the common cuckoo weighs just 3.4 grams on average, and is about the same size as a skylark's egg, whereas a non-parasitic cuckoo of the same body weight (100 grams) would be expected to lay a 10-gram egg, like that of a mistle thrush. Such a large egg might be impossible for a small host to incubate, but our experiments showed that reed warblers would also reject these large eggs. When we parasitised reed warbler nests with mistle thrush-sized model eggs that we had painted to resemble reed warbler eggs, they were more likely to be rejected than normal-sized cuckoo eggs.

The eggs of parasitic cuckoos have another peculiarity, namely unusually strong shells compared with the eggs of non-parasitic cuckoos or the eggs of their hosts. This increased strength is partly because their shells are thicker and partly because the material is denser. For small hosts such as reed warblers, the cuckoo egg is too large for them to grasp in their bills, so they peck at the shell to try to puncture it. If they succeed in making a hole, they then drink a little of the contents so these do not spill over the other eggs and make them sticky, then they grasp the edge of the hole in their bill, pick the egg up carefully, and carry it off. A thicker shell is harder to puncture and may dissuade hosts from rejecting the egg if their motivation to reject is weak. Nevertheless, reed warblers sometimes manage to eject whole cuckoo eggs, because undamaged cuckoo eggs have been found under their nests. It's not known how they do this; they must either roll them out with their bills, or perhaps with their feet.

Thick-shelled cuckoo eggs may not only protect them from host attack, they may also reduce damage during laying. This may be especially advantageous if the female cuckoo is in a hurry or if she has to squirt the egg through a narrow nest entrance, where there will be a short drop into the nest cup.

The experiments I have described so far show that the cuckoo egg needs to resemble the reed warbler's eggs in both size and appearance to beat host defences. What about the other parts of the female cuckoo's egg-laying behaviour? To test whether these were also important to deceive hosts, we did further experiments using mimetic model eggs, painted to resemble the eggs laid by the cuckoo race that specialises on reed warblers, but now varying each part of the cuckoo's strategy in turn.

First, we examined the timing of laying. When we placed our model eggs in completed but empty reed warbler nests, before the hosts had begun to lay their clutch, all were rejected. Some were thrown out of the nest, while others were buried by building a new nest lining over the top. Very sensibly, the reed warblers adopted the rule: 'any egg appearing in the nest before I start to lay cannot be mine, so reject it.' This explains why the cuckoo waits until the hosts begin to lay before she parasitises a nest.

Once the reed warblers began their clutch, we found that the number of eggs in the nest had no effect on rejection frequency. Nevertheless, real cuckoos prefer to parasitise a nest early on during the host laying period. We found fewer reed warbler nests parasitised at the four-egg stage, or later, than expected from the proportion of nests that were vulnerable at this stage. Why is this so? Most reed warblers have clutches of four eggs, and incubation begins in earnest on the day the last egg is laid. This means that a cuckoo that laid at the four-egg stage or later would be at a disadvantage because her chick would be less likely to hatch before the host chicks, and host chicks are probably more difficult to eject than host eggs. Thus, selection has favoured cuckoos that parasitise host nests at the right stage: not too early, or the egg will be rejected, and not too late, or the egg won't hatch in time.

Most songbirds lay in the early morning. On Wicken Fen, reed warblers usually lay within an hour of sunrise, from 5 a.m. to 6 a.m. Cuckoos, by contrast, lay in the afternoon, mainly between 2 p.m. and dusk, as Edgar Chance had so painstakingly discovered. Why? Cuckoos often parasitise nests at the one-egg stage. In order to exploit these nests, they must clearly lay after the hosts, so this might explain why they lay later in the day, but not necessarily why laying is late in the afternoon. We tested if the time that a cuckoo egg appeared in the nest might influence its acceptance by placing model cuckoo eggs into reed warbler nests at dawn, and found that these were more likely to be rejected than those introduced in the afternoon. So afternoon laying is another part of the cuckoo's trickery. However, we don't know why afternoons are best. On Wicken Fen, reed warblers are less likely to be at their nests in the afternoon, so the female cuckoo may be more likely to avoid detection then, but at other sites afternoon attendance is as high as in the morning.

This brings us to perhaps the most remarkable aspect of the cuckoo's laying procedure, namely the speed of laying. Most birds spend between 20 minutes and an hour sitting on the nest when laying an egg. By contrast, a female cuckoo's visit to the host nest is amazingly quick. Edgar Chance's 'Cuckoo A' on Pound Green Common spent an average of 8.8 seconds at a pipit's nest; of eight egg layings that he timed accurately, seven were of 10 seconds or less, the fastest was an incredible 4 seconds, and the maximum was 16 seconds.

The cuckoos studied by Ian Wyllie, which parasitised reed warblers on the edge of the fens, also usually laid in about 10 seconds. However, studies of cuckoos laying in reed warbler nests in the Czech Republic show that they sometimes take longer. Arne Moksnes, Eivin Røskaft, Marcel Honza and their colleagues recorded 14 layings with video cameras, and the time spent at the host nest varied from 7 seconds to 158 seconds, with an average of 41 seconds. The actual laying, from first grasping of the host egg to remove it, to sitting in the nest to lay, to flying off, lasted on average just 13 seconds. It is not known what causes this variation; perhaps older, more experienced females are faster?

Why is the female cuckoo usually so quick? Rapid laying may reduce damage from host attacks. A favourite host in the reed beds of eastern Europe, about three times the size of the reed warbler and aptly named the great reed warbler, has been seen to fly at laying cuckoos and knock them from the nest into the water below, where they sometimes drown. Even smaller hosts, such as meadow pipits and reed warblers, may damage the cuckoo's plumage during attacks with their bills and feet. However, the secretive behaviour of the female cuckoo prior to laying also gives the impression that she is reducing the chance that she is detected. Could the sight of a cuckoo at their nest alert the hosts to reject the cuckoo egg?

Mike and I tested this idea by placing a taxidermic mount of a female cuckoo on the reed warbler nest one afternoon during the laying period, and allowing the warblers to observe it for a period of five minutes. We named our stuffed cuckoo 'Edgar' in homage to Chance, though we realised this was not a very good name for a female cuckoo. At many of the nests the reed warblers mobbed the cuckoo, flitting about within a metre, snapping their beaks, giving loud rasping calls, '*skrr . . . skrr*', and often striking the mount with their feet and bills. So ferocious were some attacks that after the first few trials we had to place a thin wire cage around Edgar to prevent her destruction. After five minutes of mobbing, we then removed the cuckoo and placed a mimetic model cuckoo egg in the nest. Our experiment, therefore, simulated a cuckoo which was so slow to lay that she had been detected by the hosts. To our delight, we found that these model eggs were much more likely to be rejected (40 per cent rejected) than those placed into nests with no prior presentation of a stuffed cuckoo (only 3 per cent rejected). The sight of a cuckoo at their nest did indeed alert the hosts to reject the cuckoo egg.

The hosts' greater motivation to reject an egg may have been partly a result of their increased general excitement, rather than a specific reaction to the cuckoo itself, because we found that presentation at reed warbler nests of a stuffed jackdaw, a nest predator, also stimulated increased rejection of model eggs. However, the stuffed cuckoo had a stronger effect. Of course, even if the increased egg rejection resulted from a generalised response to a nest intruder, it would still select for rapid egg laying by the cuckoo.

Similar experiments with stuffed cuckoos have shown that the sight of a cuckoo at the nest also stimulates increased egg rejection by meadow pipits and great reed warblers. And the video recordings at reed warbler nests in the Czech Republic revealed that real cuckoos produce the same effect. In nine cases the hosts were present when the cuckoo laid her egg, and six of these cuckoo eggs (67 per cent) were rejected, compared with none out of four cases where the hosts were absent when the cuckoo laid.

So both observations of natural egg layings and experimental presentations of stuffed cuckoos show that it pays the cuckoo to be quick to avoid alerting the hosts. The actual laying event itself, namely the muscular contractions that extrude the egg from the cloaca, is unlikely to be faster than in other species. What is extraordinary about the cuckoo is the degree to which she can control the timing of this laying event. As Edgar Chance discovered, prior to laying the female sits quietly for an hour or so on a branch overlooking the host nest. Presumably during this time her egg descends her oviduct, in readiness for laying. Most birds would spend this quiet period sitting on their nest. But if the cuckoo sat for this length of time on the host nest she would alert the hosts. So her trick is to prepare for laying on a branch nearby and to visit the host nest just for the crucial few seconds it takes to expel the egg.

The female cuckoo's ability to control the moment of egg extrusion is revealed by an incident reported in a charming letter written by Mrs Cecil Dawnay to *Country Life* magazine in 1922, which transports us back to more genteel days of the last century:

> On June 4, Whit-Sunday, while we were playing tennis on the lawn in front of our house, my nurse called from the balcony outside the nursery that a cuckoo had flown in and was sitting on the nursery floor. My sister went up and caught the cuckoo and brought it out on the lawn, where we admired it. It then gently fluttered on to my small daughter's shoulder, and there, in the gravest manner possible, laid an egg, which fell unbroken to the ground. The cuckoo had been noticed previously on a tree near the nursery window, and as it had also been noticed that a pied wagtail had a nest a few feet away from the window, in a wisteria on the house, we imagined that this nest was one in which the cuckoo had intended to deposit one of its eggs.

Edgar Chance commented on this extraordinary incident in his book *The Truth About the Cuckoo*:

> The cuckoo had no doubt intended to lay in the wagtail's nest, but being delayed and deterred by the game of tennis, she had put off going to it until she could wait no longer. In desperate plight she made her flight, missed her mark and flew through the window to land on the nursery floor. Her quietness and apparent submissiveness may have been due to a kind of partial paralysis caused by her determination to retain her egg until the last possible moment.

We might add that the fact that the egg dropped to the ground unbroken is a tribute to its thick shell. A few days later, the wagtail nest was checked again and it now contained a new cuckoo egg. So this female cuckoo seems to have been extraordinarily persistent!

Edgar Chance himself witnessed other examples of a female's ability to control her laying. In 1924, on Pound Green Common, his beloved Cuckoo A was replaced by another female, 'a stupid and incompetent bird' according to Chance, 'clumsy in her actions and a poor hand at finding and re-finding a nest'. Prior to laying, she regularly spent four or five hours on her perch, near her chosen meadow pipit nest, and then often failed to find the nest when she glided down to lay. Sometimes Chance observed her searching on the ground for an hour before she found the nest and laid, all the while being attacked by the pipits and losing many feathers as a result. One afternoon he watched her search for a meadow pipit nest, which she failed to find, then she tried for a tree pipit nest and, having failed to find that, she finally laid in a willow warbler's nest. On another occasion, she glided down to the site of a meadow pipit nest at 5.40 p.m., failed to find it and eventually laid in a tree pipit nest at 8.20 p.m. These fascinating observations show that a female cuckoo can delay the laying of her egg for up to two or three hours, if necessary. They also suggest that the skill of locating host nests, essential for rapid laying, might improve with experience.

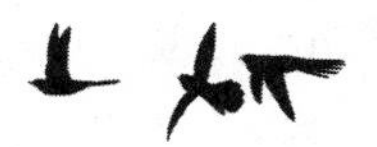

All the various parts of the cuckoo's egg-laying tactics that we have examined by experiment so far are adapted to increase the chance that the host will accept the cuckoo's egg: namely egg mimicry, egg size, the timing of laying and the speed of laying. What about the female cuckoo's habit of removing a host egg before she lays her own? Female common cuckoos usually remove one host egg, occasionally two, and very rarely three. This normally takes place immediately prior to laying, during the laying visit itself. If just one host egg is removed, the female holds it in her bill while she lays her own egg, and then she flies off with the host egg and swallows it after her departure. If two or more are removed, then the first eggs are swallowed, with a backward toss of the head, while she is at the nest, and the last is held in her bill while she lays. Occasionally, female cuckoos will remove one or two host eggs a day or two before laying, and then may remove another during the laying visit itself.

Mike and I thought that egg removal must be important for deceiving the hosts; surely the hosts would count their eggs and would easily notice if an extra egg suddenly appeared in their nest. However, to our surprise, our experiments showed that removal of a host egg was not essential for deceiving the hosts. Reed warblers were just as likely to accept one of our mimetic model cuckoo eggs when we simply added it to the clutch, rather than removing a host egg first to keep the number of eggs the same. Similarly, they were just as likely to reject non-mimetic model cuckoo eggs, regardless of whether we removed a host egg or not. Experiments with meadow pipits have also shown that egg removal has no effect on their acceptance of foreign eggs.

Why, then, does the cuckoo remove an egg? One possibility is that she is, after all, searching to remove other cuckoo eggs. If so, as we have already seen, her behaviour is not very refined; we found no tendency for a cuckoo to select a previous cuckoo egg from the clutch, whether a real one or one of our models. Nevertheless, even random removal of an egg would be better than no removal. Another possibility is that egg removal simply makes room for the cuckoo's egg and ensures there aren't too many eggs in the nest for the hosts to incubate efficiently. Our experiments support this idea, because when we added a model egg to the clutch more of the reed warbler's eggs failed to hatch than where we had removed an egg to make room for the model. This suggests that there is indeed a limit to the number of eggs the hosts can incubate.

Finally, the female cuckoo might remove an egg simply because it gives her a free meal. Why, then, doesn't she remove all the host eggs and replace them with her single egg? Our experiments show that host responses again provide the answer. When we reduced the reed warbler's final clutch size to three eggs, they never deserted. But a reduction to two eggs sometimes caused desertion, and a reduction to one egg nearly always did so. Most reed warblers on Wicken Fen lay a clutch of four, though clutches of three and five are also common. Therefore, the maximum the cuckoo can safely take from a clutch of three is one (she replaces this with her own egg, so the final clutch is three), and from a clutch of four the maximum she can take is two (two are removed, then she adds her own egg to give a final clutch of three). This argument predicts quite well the observed behaviour of cuckoos, which is to remove usually one, sometimes two host eggs, rarely more. An additional cost of removing more than one host egg, of course, is that it entails a longer stay at the host nest, and so a greater chance that the hosts will be alerted.

Although reed warblers nearly always deserted a single egg, they never deserted a single chick of their own. Their response makes good economic sense. The breeding season is short and most pairs have time to raise just one brood. If the clutch is reduced by predation to one egg, it is still early on in the nesting cycle and there is usually time to start a replacement clutch.

Much better to start again and have a good chance of raising a normal brood of four a week or two later, than devoting the whole season now to raising just one offspring. However, once the young hatch, two more weeks have passed and there is now less time available to start all over again. So it's likely to be better to persist and raise a single chick rather than none at all.

These simple economics of reed warbler reproduction have profound consequences for the evolution of cuckoo tactics. They explain very neatly why it is the cuckoo chick which has to take on the Herculean task of ejecting the host's eggs, rather than its mother earlier on during the egg laying. While there is a limit to the number of eggs the laying female can remove, because the hosts will desert a reduced clutch, two weeks later the cuckoo chick can safely eject the entire nest contents, because the hosts won't desert a reduced brood.

Our experiments with the model eggs have enabled us to dissect the cuckoo's egg-laying trickery, step by step. Each part turns out to be important in ensuring the success of her egg. The similarity in appearance and size of her egg to the host eggs helps to deceive the hosts into accepting the cuckoo egg as one of their own. The timing of laying and the removal of a host egg are important, too, to ensure the cuckoo egg is incubated efficiently and hatches in good time. And the speed of laying is essential if the cuckoo is to avoid alerting the hosts.

But now we have a puzzle to explain: if all these various tricks are necessary for cuckoo success, how did the cuckoo ever become a parasite in the first place? Presumably, the answer is that host defences and cuckoo trickery have evolved together, side by side and gradually, over the generations. So, at the start of this arms race, the hosts would have few or no defences and the cuckoo would not need the intricate trickery we see today. To test this idea, we need to take our model eggs beyond the confines of Wicken Fen, to 'play cuckoo' with other potential hosts.

6

An arms race with eggs

A female cuckoo (left) watching reed warblers in the reeds below ignores a displaying male who has landed beside her.
Wicken Fen, 9 June 2014.

Dragging a rope over the Derbyshire moors during the Easter holidays is bound to attract attention. Mike and I have been searching all day for meadow pipit nests. He holds one end of the rope, I the other, and we walk along slowly, hoping to flush sitting pipits. The rope floats lightly over the ground, like a gentle brush, and doesn't damage the vegetation or the pipit nests, which are tucked away in little hollows under tufts of grass. Even when we're sure of the exact position from where the bird flew, it's often hard to locate the nest as it is hidden so beautifully, and the dark brown eggs are well camouflaged in the shadows. We've found 23 nests today, a good day's work. To each clutch we've added a model cuckoo egg, and we'll return tomorrow to check whether the pipits have accepted them. But our nest searching has been reported to the local police, and now a policeman, in blue uniform and tall helmet, is striding over the moors towards us.

We explain that we're not *collecting* eggs, rather we are putting *extra* eggs *into* birds' nests. Not surprisingly, the policeman finds this hard to believe. Our routine of playing cuckoo now seems so normal and sensible to us, that we forget how ridiculous it must seem to someone who doesn't know why we are doing something so odd. But we describe our experiments, show him our model eggs and research permit, and he is reassured. Having checked how to spell 'cuckoo' for his record of this strange encounter, he bids us good luck and sets off back to his village beat.

In Britain, the meadow pipit is the cuckoo's favourite host in moorland. This race of cuckoo, which is the predominant one on the moors of western and northern England, in Wales and throughout Scotland, lays a brown speckled egg which matches the dark brown eggs of the pipits. Our experiments showed, just as for reed warblers in the fens, that egg mimicry was important for fooling these hosts. The pipits were more likely to reject badly matching model eggs, for example those with a paler, greyish-white background, typical of the cuckoo race that specialises on pied wagtails, or plain blue eggs, typical of cuckoos that specialise on redstarts. We often found the rejected eggs lying in the grass, just a short distance from the nest.

We also put our model cuckoo eggs into pied wagtail nests, another favourite cuckoo host in Britain, which nests in crevices in banks, rocks and walls. The greyish-white speckled eggs of its cuckoo race are a good mimic of the wagtails' eggs. Once again, we found that the mimicry was important, because the wagtails tended to reject model eggs unlike their own. Experiments with a number of other favourite hosts of the common cuckoo, for each of which there is a specialist race with a mimetic egg, also show that these hosts are particular about egg appearance and will reject badly matching eggs. Clearly then, host rejection has selected for cuckoo specialisation. The result has been the evolution of distinct races of cuckoo, each with an egg type that tends to match the eggs of its particular host species.

There is, however, a glaring exception that proves the rule – prove in the original sense of the word, namely probing or testing an idea. A favourite cuckoo host in woodland, parkland and hedgerows is the dunnock, formerly known as the hedge sparrow. Dunnocks build their nests in bushes, hedges and low trees, usually well concealed in dense vegetation. Cuckoo eggs in dunnock nests have a greyish-white background and reddish-brown spots, quite unlike the beautiful, plain turquoise-blue eggs of the dunnock. As Gilbert White remarked over 200 years ago in *The Natural History of Selborne*:

> you wonder, with good reason, that the hedge sparrows can be induced at all to sit on the egg of the cuckoo without being scandalised at the vast disproportioned size of the suppositious egg; but the brute creation, I suppose, have very little idea of size, colour or number.

No one has yet tracked cuckoos to test whether some individuals really do specialise on dunnocks, but it is likely that this is indeed a separate race of cuckoo, because DNA studies show it is genetically different from the other races that specialise on meadow pipits and reed warblers. The most extensive study of cuckoos in farmland and woodland in lowland Britain is by John Owen, who recorded an incredible 509 parasitised nests in the Felsted district, Essex, between 1912 and 1933. Of these, the dunnock was easily the most frequent victim, accounting for 302 of the parasitised nests, so it seems likely that many of the cuckoos specialised on this host. Furthermore, although the cuckoo egg in dunnock nests is clearly not mimetic – it is the wrong colour and has spots – nevertheless the egg is of a distinct type, intermediate in darkness between those of the pipit and wagtail races of cuckoo.

Why is the dunnock race of cuckoo unique among the European cuckoo races in showing no mimicry of the host eggs? The answer is clear. It's because dunnocks are the only major host species to show no egg discrimination. Our experiments show that they will accept model eggs of any colour or pattern. We wondered if dunnocks simply had poor colour vision, or found it difficult to discern egg colour in the dense cover where they build their nests. Perhaps, in a dark nest, the dunnock's own blue eggs and the various model eggs all appeared a similar shade of grey? Therefore we tested them with white or black model eggs, which were clearly different in shade, but they accepted these too. Dunnocks even accepted whole clutches of model eggs unlike their own, so their acceptance of a single model egg was not simply because they regarded it as a harmless lump of resin.

Our results with the dunnock, the odd one out among the cuckoo's favourite hosts in Europe, are illuminating. They show that a cuckoo race evolves a mimetic egg only when its host is discriminating. If dunnocks ever did begin to reject badly matching eggs, then we can be sure that their cuckoos could respond by evolving egg mimicry. There is a cuckoo race in Finland that specialises on redstart hosts, which have pure blue eggs just like those of the dunnock. This cuckoo race lays a pure blue egg, a perfect match.

We are still left with the problem of why the dunnock race of cuckoo lays a distinctive egg. Many woodland and farmland birds have pale mottled eggs. If dunnock-specialist cuckoos sometimes parasitised other species, which were discriminating, then they may have evolved a generalised match for their secondary hosts.

So far, we have assessed the match between cuckoo and host eggs by human vision. But birds have a different visual system to ours. We have three colour cones in our retinas, attuned to different wavelengths of light: long wavelengths, which we see as red; medium wavelengths, green; and short wavelengths, blue. Birds have a fourth cone type, which enables them to detect still shorter wavelengths, ultraviolet, or UV. So the blue on the crown of a male blue tit, or on the throat of a male bluethroat, will appear even more dazzling to a bird's eye than it does to our own. Experiments have shown that this UV component is important in mate choice. If UV-blocking cream is applied to the crowns of male blue tits, or to the throats of male bluethroats, then females are more reluctant to pair with them than with males who have been treated in the same way but with a control cream that does not affect UV reflectance. To human eyes, males treated with both types of cream look exactly the same. But birds can tell the difference.

Cassie Stoddard and Martin Stevens, my colleagues at Cambridge, reassessed the match between cuckoo and host eggs for various cuckoo races in Europe. First, they measured the colour match for both background colour and spot colour across the full range of wavelengths of light as perceived by a bird's eye. They found that cuckoo eggs matched their host eggs not only in the wavelengths visible to humans (blue to red), but also in the UV, visible only to the birds themselves. Then they measured the match in spot sizes between cuckoo and host eggs. These measurements enabled them to quantify the match between cuckoo and host egg, as perceived through a bird's eye.

They found that the perfection of egg mimicry in the various races of cuckoo was related to how particular their respective hosts were, as revealed by our own experiments with the model eggs. The best matches were for cuckoos with the most discriminating hosts, for example great reed warblers and bramblings. These cuckoo races have evolved wonderful mimicry of their host's eggs, with background colour, spot colour and spot sizes all copied to perfection. Moderate matches occurred where the hosts were a little less discriminating, for example reed warblers and meadow pipits. And there was no match at all when the host showed no discrimination against odd eggs, as for dunnock hosts.

Claire Spottiswoode, another Cambridge colleague, tested whether cuckoo eggs also evolve thicker egg shells in response to more strongly rejecting hosts. On average, the thickness of a cuckoo's egg shell is about a tenth of a millimetre, but their shells vary in thickness by eight-hundredths of a millimetre. This sounds trivial, but it translates to over twofold variation in breaking strength. Have thicker shells evolved to resist puncturing by more discriminating hosts? Claire compared the races of cuckoo in Britain by examining eggs in museum collections. She found that cuckoo eggs in the nests of discriminating hosts, such as reed warblers, meadow pipits or pied wagtails, had much thicker shells than those in the nests of undiscriminating dunnocks.

So in response to increasing host egg rejection, races of cuckoos have evolved eggs that are both harder to detect and harder to reject.

The arms-race analogy assumes that this wonderful cuckoo trickery has evolved gradually over the generations as hosts have gradually improved their defences. This kind of never-ending arms race has been called 'Red Queen' evolution, after the Red Queen in Lewis Carroll's *Through the Looking Glass*. In this tale, the Red Queen grabs Alice by the hand and they run together, faster and faster. To Alice's surprise, they never seem to move but remain in the same spot. 'In our country,' says Alice, 'you'd generally get to somewhere else if you ran very fast for a long time.' The Queen replies: 'A slow sort of country! Here it takes all the running you can do to keep in the same place.'

Are cuckoos and hosts engaged in such an arms race, each evolving tricks and counter-tricks to keep pace with improvements in the rival party?

Here's a fascinating 'thought experiment', one that we could dream of performing. If we could go back across the generations with our model eggs and test ancient populations of reed warblers, before they were ever subjected to cuckoo parasitism, then, according to the arms-race theory, we would expect them to have poorer defences and so to be less likely to reject eggs that differed in appearance from their own. Furthermore, if each party really had been evolving simply to keep pace with improvements in the other party, as in Red Queen evolution, then we might imagine that past cuckoos, with poor egg mimicry, might have done just as well against their past hosts, with poor egg discrimination, as current cuckoos are faring against current hosts. So as hosts improved their defences, cuckoos improved their trickery, with the result that their relative success might remain the same. As a final part of our thought experiment, we would predict that today's hosts would find the eggs of past cuckoo generations easier to detect than those of current cuckoos, because past cuckoo generations would have poorer egg mimicry.

Amazingly, this exact experiment has been done, not with cuckoos and their hosts, but with another pair of enemies, a bacterial parasite called *Pasteuria ramosa* and its host, the water flea *Daphnia magna*. This may seem a far cry from our cuckoo study, but the battle between these tiny creatures leads to a similar evolutionary arms race. Water fleas are small crustaceans, just a millimetre or two in length, that live in ponds. They feed by passing water through their mouths and filtering out tiny food particles. Sometimes they ingest harmful bacteria, such as *Pasteuria*, which attach to the gut wall and then spread through the water flea's body cavity, eventually causing it to be sterile. So infection by these bacteria reduces the water flea's reproductive success, just as acceptance of a cuckoo egg reduces the host's reproductive success.

Some genetic strains of water flea can resist the bacteria by chemical defence, which prevents them from attaching to the gut wall (a direct analogy of hosts rejecting cuckoo eggs). This then favours the evolution of bacteria that can bypass this defence, for example by mimicking the chemicals of food particles (a direct analogy of cuckoo eggs escaping detection by mimicry of host eggs). Different genetic strains of water fleas then evolve, with new chemical defences that see through this disguise (better detection), leading to new bacterial tricks (better mimicry), and so the arms race continues with further bacterial tricks and water flea defences.

Now for the wonderfully neat study that enabled a test of Red Queen evolution in this system. *Daphnia* eggs and *Pasteuria* spores can survive in a dormant state for a very long time, perhaps to enable them to survive through long periods of drought. These accumulate in pond sediments and provide a 'living fossil record' of past generations. Ellen Decaestecker and her colleagues from the Catholic University of Leuven, Belgium, sampled sediment cores from a pond which contained these resting stages over a 39-year period, which entails hundreds of generations of water fleas and bacteria. Each depth of sediment represents a 'snapshot' in the arms race, a historical record of the water flea and bacteria populations at that time. The researchers reactivated the water flea eggs and bacterial spores from across the different generations by placing them in warm temperatures and a summertime daylight regime. Water fleas could now be exposed to bacteria from the same sediment layer (contemporary bacteria) and from older sediment layers (past bacterial populations). So here is the exact equivalent of our dream experiment: comparing how hosts fare against current and past cuckoo populations.

The results showed that water fleas were less susceptible to infection by past generations of bacteria. Therefore water fleas evolved to beat old bacterial tricks, and current bacteria, in turn, evolved new tricks better able to resist host defences. However, when bacteria were pitted against their contemporary water flea populations from the same generation, there was no change in infection rates across the 39 years. So the relative success of the two parties had remained the same over time. They had indeed been 'running to stay in the same place'.

Mike and I could only dream of doing such an experiment with our cuckoos and hosts. However, although we couldn't go back in time to test if old host populations were less discriminating, we could do an equivalent experiment. Some songbirds are unsuitable as hosts of the cuckoo. There are two groups of such birds. The first group comprises species that feed their young on seeds, for example some finches. These are unsuitable as hosts because the young cuckoo needs an invertebrate diet for successful rearing. The second group has a suitable diet but nests in small holes, inaccessible to the laying female cuckoo. This group includes the tits, pied flycatchers, wheatears, starlings, house sparrows and swifts. If discrimination against foreign eggs evolves specifically in response to cuckoo parasitism, then we can predict that these unsuitable hosts will not show any egg rejection, because they have no history of interacting with cuckoos.

So Mike and I spent two summers cycling around the British countryside looking for nests of these unsuitable host species, and placing model eggs in their nests that were different from their own eggs in appearance. Our colleagues from the University of Trondheim in Norway, Arne Moksnes, Eivin Røskaft and Bård Stokke, also played the part of the cuckoo and tested unsuitable hosts with model eggs in Norway. The results of both sets of experiments revealed that these species accepted most, if not all, of the model eggs we gave them.

Some comparisons between the responses of closely related species are particularly revealing. The spotted flycatcher, whose open nest is accessible to female cuckoos, shows strong rejection of eggs unlike its own, whereas the pied flycatcher, which nests in holes and is inaccessible, shows no rejection at all. In the finch family, the two species that feed their young predominantly on invertebrates, and are therefore suitable as hosts, namely the brambling and chaffinch, show strong egg rejection, while the four species that feed their young mostly on seeds (greenfinch, linnet, redpoll, bullfinch) show little or no rejection. These comparisons suggest that rejection of eggs is not simply determined by taxonomy. Rather, it evolves only when a species becomes exploited by cuckoos.

These results show that dunnocks behave just like those species that have never had an arms race with cuckoos. Could dunnocks be recent victims, which have simply not had sufficient time to evolve egg discrimination? At first, it seems that references from old literature would argue against this view. We have already seen that over 200 years ago Gilbert White mentioned the dunnock (then called the hedge sparrow) as a host in *The Natural History of Selborne*. We can go back further to Shakespeare's *King Lear*, written in about 1605, where the Fool warns Lear that his selfish daughters will ruin him if he continues to dote on them, just as:

> The hedge sparrow fed the cuckoo so long,
> That it had it head bit off by it young.

Shakespeare intended this metaphorically, but there is one curious account where this actually happened. The cuckoo chick normally swallows its meal only when the delivery is complete, so it avoids injuring the foster parent as it bows deep into the chick's gape. An exception to this usually smooth operation involved a cuckoo nestling clamping its mouth too soon on the head of a hapless dunnock, which suffered fatal injury.

There is an even more ancient reference to dunnocks and cuckoos in Chaucer's poem of 1382, *The Parlement of Foules*, where Merlin chastises the cuckoo:

> thow mordrer of the heysugge on the braunche that broghte thee forth!

Heysugge is Middle English for 'hedge sparrow', and probably refers to the bird we now call the dunnock.

If the dunnock has been parasitised for at least 600 years in Britain, would we expect it to have evolved egg rejection by now? The answer is that it depends on the rate of parasitism by cuckoos, which will determine the selective advantage of egg rejection. For the past 70 years, thousands of bird watchers have completed nest record cards for the scheme administered by the British Trust for Ornithology (BTO). Largely because of their efforts we have a good picture of cuckoo parasitism rates. During the period 1939 to 1982, before the recent crash in the cuckoo population, the parasitism rates over the whole of Britain for the three main hosts were:

5 per cent for reed warblers (out of 6,927 nests recorded)
3 per cent for meadow pipits (out of 5,331 nests)
2 per cent for dunnocks (out of 23,352 nests)

These figures suggest that dunnocks now suffer similar pressure from cuckoo parasitism as reed warblers and meadow pipits, two hosts which have evolved egg rejection. Surely, then, dunnocks should also reject cuckoo eggs.

We can calculate how long it would take a dunnock population to evolve egg rejection, with just 2 per cent parasitism by cuckoos. The answer is several thousand generations. The reason it takes so long is that 98 per cent of nests are not parasitised, so in the vast majority of cases an inability to reject an odd egg is not penalised. Only in 2 per cent of the nests would 'rejector' dunnocks gain an advantage. Several thousand generations is just a blink of an eye on an evolutionary timescale, and many traits we see will have taken at least this long to evolve. Nevertheless, there have been profound changes in the countryside during the past few thousand years. Most of Britain was covered in woodland until a few thousand years ago, and dunnocks are not common in this habitat. Perhaps they did not become a favourite victim of the cuckoo until extensive forest clearance occurred 6,500 to 2,500 years ago, creating the woodland edges and hedgerows where dunnock populations are most dense. So it's possible that dunnocks are, indeed, relatively recent hosts that simply have not yet had time to evolve defences against cuckoos.

What have we learned from playing cuckoo with our model eggs? Our results enable us to reconstruct the likely stages of the egg arms race between cuckoos and hosts:

(1) At the start of the arms race, hosts accept eggs unlike their own (species with no history of cuckoo parasitism, the unsuitable hosts, exhibit no egg rejection). And cuckoos have no egg mimicry (in the absence of host rejection, cuckoos do not produce mimetic eggs, as shown by the cuckoo race that specialises on dunnocks).
(2) Once the cuckoo begins to parasitise a host species, any hosts that reject cuckoo eggs will raise more of their own offspring, compared with those that accept and get lumbered with raising cuckoos instead of their own young. If offspring inherit their parents' behaviour, the rejection habit will increase in the host population by natural selection. Therefore, in response to cuckoo parasitism, hosts evolve egg rejection (most cuckoo hosts reject eggs unlike their own).
(3) As hosts begin to reject eggs unlike their own, those cuckoo eggs which, by chance, resemble the host eggs more closely will be more likely to escape host detection and produce young cuckoos. If daughter cuckoos inherit their mother's egg type, better-matching cuckoo eggs will now increase in the cuckoo population by natural selection. Therefore, as hosts evolve egg rejection, cuckoos evolve egg mimicry (cuckoo races show egg mimicry when their hosts reject non-mimetic eggs).
(4) As a host evolves better egg discrimination, its cuckoo race evolves better egg mimicry (where hosts are more discriminating, the cuckoo's egg mimicry is better).

So both parties have evolved in response to the other, a case of co-evolution.

But egg mimicry by cuckoos and egg rejection by hosts is only part of the egg arms race. Natural selection has another game to play with egg markings, involving signatures and forgeries. Our field experiments have only just begun.

7

Signatures and forgeries

A female reed warbler inspecting her clutch.
Wicken Fen, 22 June 2014.

On 8 June 1938, Charles Swynnerton died at the age of 60 when his three-seater plane crashed in Tanganyika Territory, present-day Tanzania. He was on his way to Dar es Salaam to be awarded the CMG (Commander of the Order of St Michael and St George) for his pioneering work on the control of tsetse flies, large biting flies which transmit human sleeping sickness and animal disease over much of tropical Africa.

Swynnerton was born in Lowestoft, Suffolk. He emigrated to Africa at the age of 20, first managing a farm in Southern Rhodesia (now Zimbabwe), then becoming the first game warden in Tanganyika before his appointment there as director of tsetse research. He was a wonderful naturalist, collecting many specimens for the British Museum during his travels, and he had a keen interest in African cuckoos, noting that their interactions with hosts provided an opportunity to 'watch natural selection at work'.

In 1918, he published a paper in the ornithological journal *Ibis*, reporting the results of his experiments showing that many African songbirds rejected the eggs of other species and concluding, as Stuart Baker had done in 1913, that: 'selection by foster parents may have brought about the very close resemblances between the eggs of cuckoos and their hosts.' Swynnerton then went on to make an original and brilliant proposal:

> With the growth of discrimination on the part of the species most victimized . . . would come mimicry. I doubt

> whether this would always end the matter, for, when a cuckoo's egg became indistinguishable from its hosts, variation in the latter would still afford some means of distinguishing it from the cuckoo's, and it is even imaginable that a race may . . . have taken place between the host's eggs and those of the overtaking cuckoo. High distinctiveness might sometimes have been the result. In other cases sheer variability would help much to baffle the cuckoo . . . and the influence of parasitic birds has thus contributed much, in the course of ages, towards the production of that quality of diversity that to-day so characterizes passerine eggs.

Before Swynnerton, it had been assumed that the colour and spotting of birds' eggs was simply a means of camouflage. Here was a completely new idea, that colour and markings evolve as 'signatures' to protect hosts from cuckoo parasitism. Spots and squiggles might be the way that hosts write on their eggs: 'this is my egg.' The cuckoo then has to forge the host's signature by writing on its egg: 'and so is this.' An evolutionary arms race would ensue, as hosts evolve new signatures to escape the cuckoo, and cuckoos evolve to keep track with new forgeries.

This is an exact analogy of the human battle between bankers and cheats, which has led to the complex markings on our banknotes and credit cards. Counterfeiting is as old as money itself, with counterfeit coins already in circulation at around the time the first coins were introduced in the West, some 2,500 years ago. Counterfeits have had a profound influence on the design of coins and banknotes. Consider the Bank of England's £10 note, for example. It has eight features which make it difficult to forge. There are portraits of Queen Elizabeth on the front and Charles Darwin on the reverse, with fine detail on the Queen's crown and in Darwin's flowing beard. The note is covered in other fine lines with complex patterns, including micro-lettering. It is made from special paper, so has an unusual feel. The print is raised, another feature distinctive to the touch. There is a metallic thread embedded in the note, which shows as a continuous dark line when held up to the light. There is also a watermark, with another image of the Queen. A number 10 appears in red and green when the note is examined under ultraviolet light. Finally, there is a hologram on a foil patch on the front of the note that, on tilting, alternates between images of Britannia and the number 10.

Despite such complex signatures, forgeries sometimes proliferate, and so the notes have to be changed every few years. The £20 note with the picture of the composer Edward Elgar, introduced in 1999, had to be withdrawn in 2010 because forgeries had become so common and it was replaced with a new note, bearing the portrait of the economist Adam Smith. The bank's security advice is: take time to check, look and feel the note, do not rely on one single feature, and if in doubt compare with a note you know is genuine.

Do host and cuckoo eggs also bear the stamp of an evolutionary past involving signatures and forgeries? Let's first consider how a bird's egg is pigmented. To do so, we need to follow the events inside the female's reproductive tract, from ovulation to laying, which in a typical bird takes about 24 hours. The ovum, a single cell, is released from the ovary and is then fertilised soon afterwards at the top of the oviduct. As it descends the oviduct, it is covered in albumen, the familiar 'white' of a cooked egg, and with protective membranes. Four hours after ovulation, it arrives towards the bottom of the oviduct where there is a pouch, the shell gland. Here it resides for the next 20 hours. The shell gland first secretes the hard calcium-rich outer shell. Then the pigments responsible for the background colour and patterning are deposited on the outer surface in the final four hours before laying.

The two main pigments are protoporphyrin, which gives the shell a brownish hue, and biliverdin, which generates blue and green colours. Chemical analysis of the eggs of common cuckoos and their hosts, by Mark Hauber from the City University of New York and his colleagues, has shown that the colour match between the eggs of various cuckoo races and their respective host species involves matching the concentrations of these two key eggshell pigments. For example, the match of the host's brown and green eggs by cuckoos specialising on great reed warblers involves matching the concentration of protoporphyrin. And the perfect match of the plain blue host egg by cuckoos specialising on redstarts is achieved by matching the high concentration of biliverdin.

It is not known exactly how the various patterns on the shell are produced. They are likely to depend on the speed of the egg's passage and on its rotation through the shell gland. For example, slow passage would give more time for pigment to be applied and might result in spots, while rapid passage might produce streaks and rotation would lead to squiggles. The egg then passes through the lower end of the oviduct and is laid blunt end first. Genetic differences in egg colour and patterns would arise due to the way genes influence the production of the various pigments and how the egg passes through the shell gland.

How would we expect host eggs to evolve if their patterns were signatures to improve the detection of cuckoo eggs? The most obvious prediction is that there should be more variation in egg markings between females in species that are cuckoo hosts than in species that have never been parasitised by cuckoos. If each female has her own distinctive egg signature, it will then be easier for her to detect a foreign egg, just as our unique signatures can be used to certify our identity or mark our possessions. More variation in markings between different females within the host population would make life harder for the cuckoo, because there is now no one universal match that would fool all the hosts.

Bård Stokke and colleagues from the University of Trondheim, Norway, measured the variability in egg patterns of many different species in museum collections. They found that, as predicted, species that are hosts of common cuckoos in Europe have particularly variable eggs. Furthermore, host species with more variable eggs are better at rejecting foreign eggs. This suggests that variable egg patterns have indeed evolved as host signatures to beat the cuckoo.

Both reed warblers and meadow pipits have variation in individual egg markings, which must help them to recognise their own eggs, but their signatures are modest compared with those of some cuckoo hosts in Africa, where the arms race is likely to be much older. Perhaps it is no surprise that Swynnerton's insight came from the eggs of African birds. The award for the most spectacular signatures of all must surely go to an African warbler, the tawny-flanked prinia. This little brown bird is one of the favourite hosts of the cuckoo finch, a finch with cuckoo-like habits which lays its eggs in the nests of other birds. Just like the common cuckoo, the cuckoo finch has evolved into distinct races, each specialising on one particular host species. The young cuckoo finch doesn't eject the host's eggs, but it is larger than the host's own young and soon outcompetes them for food, so the host chicks die within a day or two. Therefore, the result is the same as for hosts of the common cuckoo; if the prinias fail to spot foreign eggs they lose everything and end up raising only large parasitic chicks.

Just as the work of Edgar Chance has laid the foundations for modern studies of common cuckoos and their hosts, so the remarkable story of prinia egg signatures begins with an egg collection. Major John Colebrook-Robjent was born in England in 1935, and he developed a passion for egg collecting as a schoolboy. During his army career, he served in Uganda with the King's African Rifles when Idi Amin was the regimental sergeant major, and then in 1966 he was seconded to the Zambian army. After a couple of years, he resigned his commission and began tobacco farming in Choma, southern Zambia, where he remained until his death in 2008. Here, he paid his farm workers extra wages for finding nests and collecting eggs, amassing a vast private collection of some 14,000 clutches, all carefully labelled and documented, and now bequeathed to the British Museum.

In May 2004, Claire Spottiswoode, then a young research student from the Zoology Department of Cambridge University, drove the 2,700 kilometres from her home in Cape Town to Choma, a three-day dusty journey in an old pick-up truck. She had heard rumours of the Major's amazing egg collection and had written to him wondering if she might visit to discuss the possibility of setting up a field study of African brood-parasitic birds, especially the cuckoo finch, the species least known of all. The Major was welcoming, once he had been assured that Claire wasn't an agent intent on prosecuting him for illegal egg collecting. In fact, he had permits for at least some of the clutches, and some years earlier, when correspondence with an egg collector in England had led to his prosecution in Zambia, the judge at the magistrate's court in Choma pronounced with great solemnity that the Major was not only innocent, but also a 'professor of ornithology', whose work was of great benefit to Zambia, and he was acquitted of all charges.

So began a remarkable collaboration between the ageing Major with habits of a bygone age, captivated by the beauty of his collection, and a young biologist wanting to discover how such beauty could have evolved. Among the collection were 158 clutches of tawny-flanked prinias, all taken from the Major's farm and the adjoining fields. Thirty of these clutches had been parasitised by a cuckoo finch, whose egg the Major had identified by its slightly larger size and more rounded shape. Adult cuckoo finches are seldom seen, but the collection revealed that they were abundant, and just like cuckoos must be very secretive.

The Major's neat, hand-written diaries reveal his meticulous record keeping and a fascination for variation in egg colour. These extracts from 1988 all refer to tawny-flanked prinia nests, with the clutch size (c) indicated for each one. He refers to the cuckoo finch by its old name, cuckoo weaver.

3 January: Fred I, a small boy, collects nest with c4 (egg with a blue ground).
6 January: Moses, a small boy, collects nest with c3 (white ground eggs) and Levi collects c3 (brownish-olive ground).
7 January: Dunne, one of my young labourers, collects another nest with c3 (pale salmon egg).
17 January: At last my patience is rewarded, Fred I brings in a nest containing 2 eggs, one a Cuckoo Weaver's (erythristic), host (p. buffy-olive).
7 February: Lazaro finds nest with a single egg which he correctly identifies as a Cuckoo Weaver's (cream, blotched, rufous brick).

14 December: Journey to Livingstone, in order to engage a new lawyer to represent me in my trial in Choma.
22 December: The court was well attended . . . Mr Kalima considered my work to be of great benefit to ornithology . . . I was given an Absolute Discharge . . . All eggs were returned to me . . . a most gratifying result after three and a half months of trauma . . . and a waste of precious ornithological opportunities.
25 December: Christmas at home, with 8.5 kg turkey for lunch at 4 p.m.
30 December: Levi finds nest with c2 (white ground). Small boy (Fred I) finds nest with c3 (ground pale blue).

The Major knew that individual female tawny-flanked prinias always laid the same egg type, because whenever a replacement nest appeared in the same territory after a clutch had been collected, the eggs were always identical in colour and pattern. However, among different females there was astonishing variation. Ground colour varied continuously, from white to red to olive to blue. The markings varied too, from fine spots to large blotches to intricate scribbles. Some females had mainly one type of marking on their eggs, while others had a variety of markings. Finally, the dispersion of these markings varied: some eggs had markings spread evenly over the shell surface, others had them mainly concentrated at the blunt end.

Claire invited her colleague from Cambridge, Martin Stevens, an expert in bird vision, to join her in quantifying these various colours and patterns. First, they used a spectrophotometer to measure colour across all the wavelengths of light that are detectable to a bird's eye. Then they measured the sizes of the markings and how these were dispersed over the surface of the shell. When they examined the four signature characteristics – background colour, marking type, marking variation and marking dispersion – they found that the four varied independently of one another. This is exactly what we would expect if evolution has maximised the diversity of signatures that are possible.

Do the prinias use their individual signatures to help them detect a foreign egg? Following the tradition begun by the Major, Claire paid the local farm workers to look for nests, but this time they had strict instructions not to collect the eggs but to leave them untouched. Tawny-flanked prinias build their nests among leaves in low vegetation. Like the reed warbler's, their nest is a work of art. The prinia pecks a series of holes along the edges of two neighbouring leaves and then, using its beak as a needle, it stitches the edges together with thin strips of grass to form a cradle. The nest is then suspended and stitched inside, a loosely woven oval constructed from grass, with a side entrance. The trick for finding a prinia territory is to listen out for their alarm calls and then watch the birds fly back to the nest. The searchers ranged from 10 to 80 years in age and the champions were a gang of five schoolboys, who checked nests every day after school during their seven-kilometre walk back home.

To test whether prinias would reject a foreign egg, Claire replaced one egg in the clutch with an egg of another female. Many of these were promptly rejected; the owner of the nest punctured the egg and carried it away. By comparing the characteristics of rejected and accepted foreign eggs, Claire and Martin's measurements revealed that the hosts paid attention to all four signature cues. A marked difference from their own eggs in any one cue was sufficient to cause rejection, but the prinias integrated information from all four cues, so smaller difference across several cues would lead to rejection too.

Clearly the cuckoo finch would need an outstanding match to fool such particular hosts. So it was thrilling to discover from the Major's egg collection that the race of cuckoo finch that specialises on tawny-flanked prinias had a corresponding range of variation in its eggs, a set of forgeries which matched, almost to perfection, the range in signatures of its host. These parasite forgeries matched the host signatures across the full spectrum of light wavelengths perceived by a bird's eye. Obviously the ideal female cuckoo finch should target those prinia individuals for whom her forgery was the perfect match. But Claire and Martin found that cuckoo finches parasitised nests haphazardly with respect to the host egg type and, as a result, many of their eggs were rejected. Only when there was an occasional match, by chance, did the cuckoo finches succeed in tricking the hosts. So the variable signatures of the prinias were a wonderfully effective defence against parasitism.

Is the signature-forgery arms race continuing today? Comparing eggs collected by the Major over the past four decades, it was clear that both colours and patterns have changed even over a short time period. In some of the measures, particularly colour, cuckoo finch eggs and host eggs have changed in concert, so cuckoo finch eggs are a better match of contemporaneous host eggs. This suggests that new parasite forgeries have tracked new host signatures through time. However, the tracking is not perfect. For example, there is a rare host egg type, with an olive-green background, that the cuckoo finch has not yet forged. Females with this signature have become more common over the last 40 years, presumably because they are better able to detect any parasite eggs and so raise more of their own offspring, who inherit the same effective signature. This egg type should continue to proliferate until a new forgery appears. It will be fascinating to track these changes in the future, now with the advantage of digital photography rather than by egg collecting, as parasite forgeries follow host signatures in a never-ending evolutionary chase.

What would happen to egg signatures if a host ever became freed from parasitism? The ideal test would be to take some individuals of a cuckoo host species and release them on an island where there are no cuckoos. We would need an island to be sure that the birds did not disperse, so we could follow their descendants over time. The prediction is that in the absence of parasitism the distinctive egg signatures would gradually diminish, because they would no longer be needed.

Amazingly, this experiment has already been done, though it began in shameful circumstances. In Africa, village weaverbirds are favourite hosts of the diederik cuckoo, a bird the size of a European starling. The male cuckoo is a beautiful metallic green above, white below, with a striking red eye and a persistent call: '*dee-dee-deedereek*'. During the eighteenth century, the Atlantic slave trade reached its peak, with ships ferrying cargoes of slaves from West Africa to work in the sugar plantations of the West Indies. The slave ships routinely brought over captive birds, too. On the island of Hispaniola, the French ladies liked to wear bird feathers in their hats, and it was also the fashion to walk around town with small birds in a hand-held cage. In 1797, Médéric Louis Élie Moreau de Saint-Méry reported:

> I have had occasion to admire several times more than 200 birds of different species, all having come from Sénégal. They were small and dressed in very pretty clothes, and with pleasantly nuanced and vivid colours.

Village weaverbirds must have survived the ocean crossing particularly well, and must have taken well to captivity, too, perhaps because in Africa they were used to feeding on food scraps near human habitation. According to one account, a woman in Port-au-Prince, named Madam Sagá, was famous for having a large number of them. Her legacy remains in that Madam Sagá (in Spanish), or Madame Sara (in French) is still a common name for the village weaverbird on Hispaniola today. Inevitably, some weaverbirds escaped. They thrived in their new home, spread rapidly and, just as they did back in Africa, bred in large colonies, with up to 150 nests per tree. But on the island there was an important change to their lives: there were no cuckoos in the West Indies. It is a cruel irony that the journey across the Atlantic led to freedom for these birds but to slavery for their human companions.

In Africa, diederik cuckoos have a hard time successfully parasitising village weaverbirds, because these hosts are very good at rejecting any egg that is not a perfect match of their own eggs. Just like the tawny-flanked prinias, their ability to spot a foreign egg is enhanced by remarkable variation in their egg signatures. An individual female village weaverbird lays one constant egg type throughout her life, but the pattern varies among females: the ground colour varies from white to turquoise blue to emerald green, and eggs can be either plain or speckled. In experiments where one host egg was removed and replaced with an egg of another female, it was found that females were quick to reject eggs that differed from their own in either background colour or spotting. Rejected eggs were pecked open and then carried off, usually within a day of experimental parasitism, but sometimes within a few minutes.

On Hispaniola, the introduced village weaverbirds have been free from cuckoo parasitism for about 200 years, equivalent to about 100 generations. Have their egg signatures become less distinct since they no longer face a threat from cuckoos? David Lahti, from the City University of New York, visited Hispaniola in 2001. He measured the egg colours from over 150 clutches of village weaverbirds, using a spectrophotometer that assessed reflectance across all the wavelengths visible to a bird's eye. He also took careful measurements of spotting patterns, including the size of the spots, their density and their dispersion over the egg. He then compared these measurements with those he had made two years earlier from over 100 clutches of eggs in the ancestral populations of West African village weaverbirds.

Collecting all this information from the two populations on either side of the Atlantic was a heroic task, not least because the weavers suspend their nests from thin branches in tall trees, often 10 metres above the ground. In Hispaniola David could use tall ladders, but in the remote parts of the Gambia, West Africa, he often had to climb freely or with ropes. This would always attract a large crowd of curious onlookers from the local village, some only too keen to help, once they had heard of David's interest in the birds. During one of his climbs, a villager standing below with a rifle shot several weavers out of the tree while another, equally well-meaning, found a large colony of nests nearby and cut the tree down. Once the nests were reached, there were further hazards. The village weaverbird's nest is kidney-shaped, woven from leaf strips and with an entrance on the underside. As David felt inside for eggs, he soon discovered that the nests were a favourite resting site for snakes. Most were harmless egg-eating snakes, but once he reached into a nest, felt scales and pulled his hand out quickly. Immediately, a boomslang, one of the most deadly snakes in Africa, shot out.

David survived, and his results are fascinating. With freedom from cuckoo parasitism, the egg signatures of the village weaverbirds on Hispaniola have indeed become less distinct. Compared with the parasitised weaverbirds back in Africa, their clutches are much less variable in ground colour and spotting. Furthermore, individuals now have more variation within their own clutches. So not only have their signatures become less individually distinct, they are also reproduced less faithfully on their own eggs. This last finding is particularly interesting, because it could be argued that the introduced populations have less variable clutches simply because they were founded from a small number of individuals who, by chance, did not have the full range of variation in the source population (known as the 'founder effect'). However, this could not explain why variation within a clutch has increased, which surely reflects an evolutionary loss of signature consistency.

David Lahti then tested whether poorer signatures in Hispaniola compromised the weaverbirds' ability to reject foreign eggs. He tested birds by presenting them with another weaverbird's egg, as in previous experiments with village weaverbirds back in West Africa. He found that the weaverbirds in Hispaniola were just as likely to reject a foreign egg with a given difference from their own in colour and spotting. But because their own eggs were no longer so distinctly different from the eggs of other females, the overall rejection frequency of foreign eggs was much lower than in the African populations. Therefore the decline in egg rejection was entirely a result of their poorer egg signatures, which made it harder to recognise a foreign egg.

The same results were found for another population of village weaverbirds, introduced in 1886 to the cuckoo-free island of Mauritius in the Indian Ocean from a source population parasitised by diederik cuckoos in southern Africa. This second island population had been free from cuckoo parasitism for a shorter time, just 115 years or about 60 generations, when Lahti made his measurements in 2000–2001. Once again, he found that egg signatures had become less distinct compared with the source population, and as a result the island weaverbirds were less able to recognise a foreign egg. The changes were less marked than in Hispaniola, exactly as we would expect from a more recent introduction, with less time for evolutionary change.

Why did village weaverbirds lose their egg signatures so rapidly? Perhaps signatures not only have no advantage once the threat of cuckoo parasitism is removed, but become positively disadvantageous. Birds might incur two costs from signatures on their eggs. The first is simply the cost of making the signatures, equivalent to the bank's expense of making complicated patterns on banknotes. The second is that by signing its egg with new, distinct colours and patterns, the bird might end up with an egg that is more distinguishable from a cuckoo egg, but one that is less well camouflaged, or less well adapted to other hazards.

David Lahti's measurements suggest that village weaverbird eggs are threatened not only by cuckoos but also by solar radiation. In sunnier parts of Africa, their eggs have a more intense blue-green colour (due to more biliverdin pigment), which helps protect them from damage by ultraviolet light and from overheating. Therefore, the evolution of paler background colours and spotting, to give more distinctive signatures, might compromise the best defence against the sun's rays. In support of this idea, once the threat of cuckoos had gone, the island populations of weaverbirds evolved eggs with a more uniform intense blue-green colour. Therefore, whenever hosts evolve signatures as a protection against cuckoos they are likely to pay a price because signatures will reduce their eggs' protection against other threats.

Charles Swynnerton would surely have been thrilled to know that his signature hypothesis had triumphed, and that African birds had provided the key evidence. But we still have a puzzle to explain. Village weaverbirds and tawny-flanked prinias are experts at rejecting eggs that differ from their own; but how do they know what their own eggs look like?

One rule the hosts could use is discordancy, namely: 'reject the odd one out.' However, village weaverbirds are just as likely to reject a foreign egg from a clutch of two. Furthermore, if they are given two foreign eggs plus one of their own, so that their own egg is now the odd one out, they still reject the two foreign eggs. Remarkably, they will even reject a whole clutch of foreign eggs, with none of their own available for comparison. These, and similar experiments with other host species, suggest that hosts know what their own eggs look like.

The most likely way hosts could come to know their own eggs, especially when complex signatures are involved, is by learning. Arnon Lotem, from Tel Aviv University, discovered that individuals of one host species learn their egg type during the laying of their very first clutch. They then remember the pattern and use this as a standard for discriminating against foreign eggs. Lotem's elegant field experiments involved great reed warblers, a favourite host of the common cuckoo across a large geographical range, from continental Europe through Asia to Japan. Only female great reed warblers incubate, and so only females make decisions concerning egg rejection, which simplified the analysis.

The experiments involved presenting females with a painted, plain brown egg, very different from their own eggs, which have a pale green background and spots. Old females, who had bred before, rejected the brown egg at whatever stage it was added to the clutch – either early on when the female had laid just one egg, or later, when she had completed her clutch of four or five eggs. By contrast, young females, breeding for the first time, tended to accept a brown egg placed in their nests early on during laying, but rejected one added after clutch completion. This suggests that learning occurs during the laying of the first clutch, and that young females had been fooled by the experiment to include an early brown egg as one of their own type.

The key experiment involved getting up very early in the morning and replacing each of a young female's eggs, soon after laying, with a brown painted egg. So these young females were prevented from normal exposure to their own eggs, and instead experienced a clutch of brown eggs in their nest. These young females accepted the brown clutch, apparently having learnt them as their own. Most old females, however, were not tricked by this procedure and rejected the clutch of brown eggs, implying they had remembered their own eggs from previous breeding attempts. Interestingly, a few old females did accept the brown clutch, but if they were given a single egg of their own this seemed to jog their memory, and they then immediately rejected all the brown eggs.

Young great reed warblers clearly 'imprint' on their first clutch. However, they did not reject one of their own eggs after they had imprinted on a clutch of brown eggs. One possibility is that they had some brief, but sufficient, exposure to their own eggs before these were replaced experimentally with the brown eggs. Alternatively, they may have an innate preference to learn egg types similar to their own, and so are prepared to accept their own eggs even at a later stage. A predisposition to learn one's own species' patterns is evident in another context, namely song learning. In aviary experiments, young birds will sometimes learn the song of another species, but if they are given a choice they prefer to learn their own species' song. Perhaps birds are predisposed to learn particular visual patterns, too.

These discoveries of how birds learn what their own eggs look like have fascinating implications for the arms race between cuckoos and hosts. The problem that arises from having to learn your own eggs is clearly that of imprinting on the wrong type. This occurred in the experiments, but will also happen in nature whenever a cuckoo parasitises a first-time breeder early on during the laying of the clutch, because the naive host will then be tricked into learning the cuckoo's egg type as one of its own. The host would then be doomed to accept that foreign egg type for the rest of its life.

An obvious way of avoiding this mistake would be to imprint only on the first-laid egg. This would ensure the host learned what its egg looked like before any cuckoo had a chance to lay. This would work beautifully if there were no variation in the host's own eggs, because the first egg would provide a perfect picture of what all the other eggs would look like. If a female's eggs were variable, however, then she would need to prolong learning to make sure that she got to know all the various shades or spotting patterns of her own eggs. Arnon Lotem suggests this is why great reed warblers imprint on a whole clutch rather than just their first egg. The best compromise may be to prolong learning until the host has been exposed to a range of its own eggs, despite the occasional cost of mis-imprinting on a cuckoo egg if the host is unlucky and gets parasitised during the learning period. In general, learning should be more prolonged the more variable the host's own eggs and the lower the chances of parasitism. Experiments are needed to test these ideas.

Discriminating cuckoo eggs involves two stages. So far, we have examined the first stage, namely how the hosts recognise a foreign egg. The answer is that they learn the complex signatures of their own eggs so that they can recognise foreign eggs with a different pattern. In effect, they follow that security advice from banks to customers: do not rely on one single feature, and if in doubt compare a suspected forgery with a signature you know is genuine.

The second stage is the decision to accept or reject. Imagine that the hosts notice an egg slightly different from their learnt set: should they reject it? It could be a cuckoo egg, but it could be one of their own, perhaps a rare type they have not seen before, or one that got soiled in the nest lining. A sensible host should take account not only of the appearance of a suspect egg but also of the probability of parasitism. Just as we are more likely to lock our doors and guard our possessions when there are thieves at large, so hosts should vary their rejection threshold depending on how they assess the risks of parasitism.

We have already encountered evidence that hosts are cautious about egg rejection. Several hosts, including reed warblers, are more likely to reject a cuckoo egg if they see a cuckoo at their nest, either a real one or a stuffed cuckoo in an experiment. Why do hosts need to be alerted in this way? Why not always reject? The host's caution would make sense if they sometimes made mistakes and rejected one of their own eggs. Perhaps the risk of a mistake is worthwhile only when the hosts have good reason to believe that a cuckoo has laid an egg in their nest.

Our observations on Wicken Fen show that reed warblers do indeed risk making mistakes when they reject eggs. First they make recognition errors. When there was a well-matching cuckoo egg in their nest, either a real cuckoo egg or one of our mimetic model eggs, the reed warblers got it right and ejected the foreign egg at 70 per cent of the nests, but they made a mistake at the other 30 per cent of the nests and threw out one of their own eggs rather than the cuckoo egg. Strong evidence that these are recognition errors comes from the fact that reed warblers did not make this mistake when the model egg in the nest was clearly different from their own. Other studies have also shown that hosts are more likely to make recognition errors when cuckoos have highly mimetic eggs.

Second, hosts sometimes eject one of their own eggs even when they are not parasitised. These false alarms are also inevitable when the host's recognition system is not perfect. So hosts have a conundrum. As they increase the chance of getting rid of cuckoo eggs, by throwing out a suspect egg, they will inevitably incur the cost of more false alarms.

What should the hosts do? The obvious answer is they should vary egg rejection depending on the risks of parasitism. If there are many cuckoos about, and so the risk of parasitism is high, they should be more particular and reject even the slightest suspect egg. They will make more false alarms as a consequence, but this is a price worth paying in order to save parasitised clutches from destruction by a cuckoo chick. On the other hand, if there are few cuckoos in the vicinity, they should be more relaxed. An unfamiliar egg is now more likely to be one of the host's own eggs. So the finding that hosts are more likely to reject an egg when they see a cuckoo at their nest makes very good sense. If the risk of parasitism is high, hosts should be more likely to treat a suspect egg as a cuckoo egg rather than one of their own.

A host's life is not easy! Every step the hosts make to improve their defences is met by better cuckoo trickery. In response to cuckoo parasitism, hosts evolve egg rejection, but cuckoos reply by evolving egg mimicry. Hosts then evolve more complex egg signatures, but cuckoos, in turn, evolve good forgeries. We now conclude that, faced with problems in recognising cuckoo eggs, hosts should look out for adult cuckoos so they can vary their egg rejection in relation to parasitism risk. It will come as no surprise that adult cuckoos try to thwart hosts at this stage, too. They do so partly by being secretive. But they have another trick, too, namely to avoid host recognition by coming in various guises.

8

A cheat in various guises

A female cuckoo, hidden in an ash tree, watching a pair of reed warblers. She parasitised their nest five days later.
Wicken Fen, 9 June 2014.

The heroes of this chapter are two of the greatest naturalist explorers of all time. On 20 April 1848, Henry Walter Bates and Alfred Russel Wallace set sail from Liverpool on the ship *Mischief*. Five weeks later, they entered the mouth of the Amazon and, as Bates recorded in his journal, they saw 'the beauties of a tropical country for the first time'. Unlike Charles Darwin, neither came from a wealthy family, and to fund their expeditions they relied on selling the specimens they found to the British Museum and to professional collectors. Bates and Wallace spent much of their first year together in the forests. Their daily routine was to rise at dawn to study birds and mammals, then after breakfast they turned their attention to insects until the early afternoon, when they sought shelter from the heat of the day. In the evenings they made notes and preserved their specimens.

Wallace's return to England after four years met with disaster. Three weeks into the voyage home, his ship caught fire. Along with the rest of the crew, he scrambled to safety in the lifeboats, but then watched in horror as, back on board, all his precious specimens and journals went up in flames. He was rescued 10 days later by a passing ship, claimed the insurance money on his lost specimens, and within 18 months, and with admirable lack of self-pity, was off to the Malay Archipelago on another collecting trip. Meanwhile, Bates stayed on in the Amazon until 1859, spending 11 long years in the forests and amassing over 14,700 specimens (mainly insects) of which over 8,000 were new to science. He sent them home on three separate ships to guard against the calamity suffered by his companion.

Bates was astonished by the diversity of tropical insects and by how closely many of them resembled inanimate objects: caterpillars like twigs, moths like bark or dead leaves, beetles with wing cases that shone like dew drops. He thought that such wonderful camouflage must protect them against sharp-eyed predators. However, not all prey escaped by hiding. Some startled their enemies, such as a hawkmoth caterpillar that reared up when disturbed and dilated its body to expose two large eyes, just like a venomous snake. He showed this to the native Indian villagers, who were all terrified by the display. He was fascinated to discover, too, that some palatable species of butterflies resembled the bright colours and lazy flight of distasteful species. So good was this mimicry that even with his expert eyes he had to catch them in a net and examine them closely to determine whether they were the model (the distasteful species) or the mimic (the palatable species). He suggested this was a form of protective mimicry which fooled predatory birds.

He published his findings in 1862, three years after his return to England, in the *Transactions of the Linnean Society of London*, in a paper modestly entitled 'Contributions to an insect fauna of the Amazon valley'. Darwin's *The Origin of Species* had just been published, and Bates suggested that his discovery of mimicry of a distasteful species 'offers a most beautiful proof of the theory of natural selection'.

Darwin was thrilled and wrote to Bates, praising the paper as 'one of the most remarkable and admirable papers I ever read in my life . . . but,' he continued,

> I have one serious criticism . . . and that is the title of the paper . . . you ought to have called prominent attention in

> it to the mimetic resemblances. Your paper is too good to be largely appreciated by the mob of naturalists without souls, but rely on it, it will have *lasting* value, and I cordially congratulate you on your first great work.

Darwin was right; this form of mimicry, where an undefended species (the 'mimic') resembles a defended species (the 'model'), is widespread in the natural world. It is known as Batesian mimicry, in honour of Bates's wonderful discovery.

In February 1858, while Bates was still continuing his labours in the Amazon, Wallace lay in his hammock on the island of Ternate in the Malay Archipelago, suffering from severe bouts of fever. It was during one of these fits that the idea of natural selection came to him, in a flash. He wrote an essay on his theory and sent it to Darwin for comment. This was the famous bombshell that arrived in Darwin's post on 18 June 1858; Wallace proposed the exact same theory that Darwin himself had been working on for nearly 20 years. Their joint papers were presented to the Linnean Society just two weeks later, on 1 July 1858, and Darwin rushed to publish his great book the following year. Wallace never complained that Darwin got most of the credit, writing to Bates that 'I could never have approached the completeness of his book.' In 1869, he dedicated his book *The Malay Archipelago* to Darwin, 'to express my deep admiration for his genius and his works', and 20 years later he magnanimously entitled his own volume on natural selection *Darwinism*.

It is in this book *Darwinism* that Wallace applies the insight of his friend Bates to the appearance of the cuckoo. Wallace points out that many parasitic cuckoos look remarkably similar to birds of prey, particularly *Accipiter* hawks, such as the sparrowhawk. They share a close resemblance in size and shape: an elongated body, long wings and a long tail. They have a similar plumage pattern: greyish or brownish above, paler and barred below. And they both have a swift, direct flight. This similarity in shape, plumage and flight gave rise to an ancient belief that the disappearance of cuckoos from Europe during the winter months came about because they transformed themselves into hawks. Aristotle dismissed this possibility, pointing out that cuckoos lack both talons and a hooked bill. Nevertheless, the resemblance is sufficiently close to often cause human confusion. During Edgar Chance's pioneering studies of the common cuckoo on Pound Green Common, the female that he followed closely for five seasons (Cuckoo A) was mistaken by a local villager for a sparrowhawk and was about to be shot, when Chance intervened just in time.

Hawks and cuckoos are not closely related, so why are they so similar in appearance? Wallace noted that cuckoos are 'an exceedingly weak and defenceless group of birds', and he suggested that the resemblance was an example of protective mimicry, in which cuckoos had evolved to resemble hawks to reduce hawk attacks. Wallace may be right, because cuckoos are indeed more rarely taken by hawks than expected from their abundance relative to other potential prey. Nevertheless, hawk-like plumage, with barring below, is more prevalent in parasitic than in non-parasitic cuckoo species, which suggests that it might also somehow help cuckoos in their battle to slip past host defences.

On Wicken Fen, reed warblers encounter both common cuckoos and sparrowhawks every day. Are they fooled by their similarity? To test this, Justin Welbergen and I presented taxidermic mounts next to reed warbler nests during their laying period, when they would be vulnerable to cuckoo parasitism. We found that the reed warblers were reluctant to approach a mount of a sparrowhawk. They usually had a quick look and then retreated immediately and hid in the reeds, perfectly still and silent, several metres away. Their extreme caution makes good sense, because sparrowhawks are dangerous predators of small birds. Sparrowhawks usually make surprise attacks, dashing by the edges of vegetation or along watercourses, ready to pick off any unsuspecting small birds from a perch or in flight by shooting out their long legs and grasping them in their powerful talons. They can twist and turn though dense vegetation with astonishing dexterity, and will crash through leaves and branches to make a final kill. The intensity of a sparrowhawk's hunt is beautifully captured by Kenneth Richmond's description of one standing on its kill with a 'lunatic, pitiless glare'. In a poem by Ted Hughes, the sparrowhawk announces: 'My manners are tearing off heads'.

Cuckoos cannot damage adult songbirds. Nevertheless, at some nests the reed warblers treated the cuckoo mount as if it was a sparrowhawk. They were reluctant to approach, and hid in the reeds. At other nests, however, the warblers immediately attacked the cuckoo, striking it with their bills and feet, giving loud rasping calls '*skrr . . . skrr*', and snapping their bills while they hopped about close by in agitation. Clearly, then, some pairs could tell the difference. But why were others so cautious?

To test whether it was the similarity of the cuckoo to a sparrowhawk that made some warblers cautious, we manipulated the appearance of the cuckoo mounts to vary their hawk resemblance. We did this by pinning a piece of silk below, which obscured the natural barring. The silk was either pure white (so the cuckoo no longer had hawk-like barring) or had bars made with a felt-tip pen, of the same width and spacing as natural bars (which retained the hawk-like appearance). We found that reed warblers were much more reluctant to approach and mob a cuckoo mount with barred rather than unbarred silk underparts. Therefore, the hawk-like barring did indeed deter the hosts and so would facilitate a cuckoo's access to host nests. This protective mimicry is 'Batesian' because the adult cuckoo is otherwise defenceless against host attack. However, the cuckoo is not harmless to its enemies, in the sense that a palatable butterfly is harmless to a predatory bird, because its mimicry helps it to parasitise host nests. Perhaps the cuckoo is better described as a 'parasite in wolf's clothing'.

Our experiments revealed the importance of barring for a cuckoo's hawk-like disguise, but barring is unlikely to be the only cue. In further experiments in which we modified the underparts of mounts with pieces of silk, we found that reed warblers were more afraid of a barred cuckoo than of a barred dove. Therefore other hawk-like features of the cuckoo must combine with the barring to deter the hosts. And reed warblers continued to be frightened of sparrowhawk mounts even when they were unbarred below. So, just like us, birds use a combination of features to distinguish friend from foe.

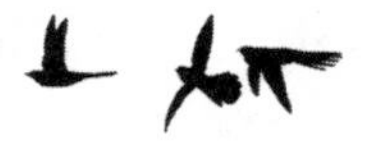

The common cuckoo, therefore, employs two forms of mimicry as it attempts to slip past host defences. First, the adult cuckoo mimics a hawk to deter host approach. This is a case of appearing dangerous, whereas in fact the adult cuckoo could safely be attacked. Second, the cuckoo egg mimics the host's eggs to avoid host rejection. This is a case of appearing harmless, whereas in fact the cuckoo egg is dangerous to host reproduction. We have already seen that if hosts see through the cuckoo's egg disguise they can save their clutch by rejecting the cuckoo egg. If hosts see through the adult cuckoo's disguise, and launch an attack, can they deter the cuckoo from laying?

Female cuckoos can certainly be very persistent, and will sometimes lay in a host nest even while they are being attacked by the hosts, as shown in the early film by Edgar Chance. Nevertheless, when Justin and I tested some 200 pairs of reed warblers with cuckoo mounts at their nests, we found that those which attacked the mount were four times less likely to be parasitised by cuckoos than those that treated the cuckoo as a sparrowhawk, and were too nervous to approach.

Why do cuckoos avoid parasitising the nests of more aggressive hosts? Cuckoos are sometimes damaged by host attacks. There is one report of a great reed warbler attacking a female cuckoo so viciously that she fell into the water below the nest and drowned. Reed warblers are only a third the size of a great reed warbler, but even they can pull out the cuckoo's feathers. However, the risk of physical damage may not be the main deterrent. When reed warblers attack a cuckoo, their loud rasp calls and bill snaps might attract predators, which would increase the chance of the cuckoo's egg being eaten. Furthermore the commotion appears to alert the whole neighbourhood: as soon as reed warblers begin to give rasp calls, other reed warblers approach from nearby territories to see what's going on. If neighbours are alerted, perhaps they would be more likely to watch out for cuckoos. And, as our previous experiments have shown, if they see a cuckoo at their nest they are more likely to reject the cuckoo's egg.

These ideas stimulated another set of experiments on Wicken Fen. First, Justin and I tested whether it really was the loud rasping calls of the reed warblers that attracted neighbours, rather than other signals, for example the movements of the reeds or the sight of the enemy itself. We placed small loudspeakers in the reeds, away from any nests, so our results would not be confounded by the calls of reed warblers themselves. When we broadcast rasp calls, '*skrr . . . skrr*', reed warblers quickly approached from up to 40 metres away. We could see the reeds twitching as the warblers climbed up the stems to peer over the tops, and then they made short flights to the speaker. Sometimes, up to six neighbours came over to investigate. When we broadcast a control call, the territorial call of a male chaffinch, '*hreet . . . hreet*', reed warblers were rarely attracted, so neighbours were alerted specifically by the alarm calls of their own species.

Next, Justin and I tested what reed warblers might learn from investigating the cause of alarms on a neighbouring territory. For this experiment, we placed a cuckoo mount next to a reed warbler's nest and alongside we placed a loudspeaker, which broadcast reed warbler rasp calls, to ensure the neighbours came to see what was going on. We used several cuckoo mounts and several different broadcasts to make sure the responses were not due to unusual features of particular mounts or broadcasts. Once again, neighbours approached, and this time they saw the cuckoo mount. It was remarkable to watch the reed warblers trespassing right into the middle of a neighbour's territory, something they would not normally dare to do. Sometimes the territory owners chased them off.

We then considered whether this eavesdropping experience affected how reed warblers responded to a cuckoo mount at their own nests. It certainly did! Having observed their neighbours mobbing a cuckoo, the warblers became much more responsive to a cuckoo on their own territory: they were quicker to approach a cuckoo mount at their own nest, and they behaved more aggressively towards it, giving many more rasp calls. Furthermore, this increase in aggression was specific to cuckoos; the reed warblers did not change their responses to mounts of other species. In effect, the hosts have a neighbourhood watch, where the word gets round that there is a particular threat at large, so everyone is on alert and defences are increased specifically to that enemy.

Let's now summarise the various host defences and cuckoo tricks that have been unravelled by these experiments:

(1) Hosts reject eggs that differ from their own in colour and pattern. In response, cuckoos evolve such good forgeries that the hosts cannot be completely certain whether they have been parasitised, simply by inspecting their clutch.
(2) Hosts therefore watch out for cuckoos to determine their risk of parasitism. If they see a cuckoo at their nest, they are more likely to reject an egg. In response, cuckoos are very secretive and quick when they lay, to avoid alerting the hosts.
(3) Hosts also attack female cuckoos, which deters the cuckoo from laying. In response cuckoos mimic hawks, which makes the hosts more wary of approaching them.
(4) Hosts now widen their source of information about local cuckoo activity, not only watching out for cuckoos on their own territory, but also listening out for whenever neighbours give alarms. If they see a cuckoo being mobbed on a neighbouring territory, they are more likely to risk close approach and to attack a cuckoo at their own nest. As we shall now see, the cuckoo combats this last host defence, too. It does so by coming in different guises.

All adult male common cuckoos are plain grey above. But females come in two plumage types, or morphs: some are grey above, like the males, while others are bright rufous. When I first saw a rufous female cuckoo flying past, I failed to recognise it for a moment because I was so used to expecting cuckoos to be grey. Could different guises baffle the hosts too?

Rose Thorogood and I tested this by presenting reed warblers with either grey or rufous cuckoos. We used wooden models this time, to be sure that the cuckoos were identical except for their colour. My artistic wife, Jan, made the models, so art and science came together for these experiments. We repeated our 'neighbourhood watch' tests, in which we presented a cuckoo at a reed warbler nest, together with the broadcast of reed warbler alarm calls, to attract neighbours. But this time we sometimes presented a grey cuckoo, sometimes a rufous cuckoo.

As before, we found that reed warblers increased defences back at their own nests if they had witnessed a neighbour mobbing a cuckoo. However, they only increased their response to the cuckoo morph that they had seen their neighbours mobbing. If they had seen neighbours mobbing a grey cuckoo, they were alerted only to grey cuckoos at their own nest, while if they had seen neighbours mob a rufous cuckoo, they were alerted only to rufous cuckoos at their own nest. Therefore, whenever hosts became alerted to one cuckoo morph, the alternative morph was more likely to be undetected.

In the fens, grey female cuckoos are much more common than rufous females. Perhaps grey females have the extra advantage of looking like sparrowhawks, while rufous females simply get an advantage from being rare, and so are less likely to be recognised as an enemy when hosts are on the lookout for grey cuckoos? However, in some other parts of Europe rufous female cuckoos are the more common morph. The reasons for this geographical variation are not yet known.

Variable plumage is characteristic of other species of parasitic cuckoo, too, and is likely to have evolved to confuse enemy recognition by hosts. Just imagine how easy it would be for us to recognise a thief if all thieves were like those in cartoons, with masks and bags labelled 'swag'. But thieves come in many guises: some are smartly dressed, some appear to be friends rather than foes. Most of us will get tricked at some time in our busy lives.

Spare a thought for the reed warblers, then, rushing to raise their brood during a short British summer. Your arch enemy sometimes appears hawk-like, but is sometimes very different in its dress; it is secretive and incredibly quick when it invades your territory; and it appears to leave no trace – no change in the number of eggs in your nest, nor in their appearance. You incubate the clutch, and then something extraordinary happens; one of the chicks throws all the other eggs out of the nest and grows to eight times your own body weight. At last, surely, you will realise you have been duped . . .

9

A strange and odious instinct

A female reed warbler (left) watching her egg being ejected from the nest, while the male waits with a fly for the young cuckoo.
Burwell Lode, 2 June 2014.

Although Aristotle mentioned that the young cuckoo 'casts out of the nest those with whom it has so far lived', his brief description seems to have been ignored or forgotten for the next 2,000 years, and the credit for discovery of the extraordinary performance is now given to Edward Jenner, the celebrated pioneer of vaccination.

In 1788, prior to his famous work on smallpox, Jenner published a paper on cuckoos in the *Philosophical Transactions of the Royal Society*, which led to his election as a Fellow of the Royal Society the following year. This is the oldest and longest-running science journal in the world. It began in 1665, just five years after the Royal Society was founded under the motto *Nullius in verba* ('take nobody's word for it'), to champion the view that the only way to establish facts was by careful observation and experiment.

The initial full title of the journal was: *Philosophical Transactions: giving some accompt of the present undertakings, studies and labours of the ingenious in many considerable parts of the world.* The 1788 volume gives an insight into the range of scientific enquiry at that time. There is a paper by Erasmus Darwin (Charles Darwin's grandfather) entitled 'Frigorific experiments on the mechanical expansion of air, explaining the cause of the great degree of cold on the summits of high mountains', one by William Herschel on his newly discovered Georgian planet (Uranus), one by Joseph Priestley on the chemical composition of water, with others on mathematics and the 'irritability of vegetables'. Alongside these is Jenner's paper, modestly entitled, 'Observations on the natural history of the cuckoo'. It is a masterpiece of meticulous observation and experiment, which rejoices in the wonders of the natural world, simply for their own sake. The paper was to cause what Edgar Chance later called 'a storm of incredulity'. This is Jenner's description of what he saw in a hedge sparrow's (dunnock's) nest on 18 June 1787:

> . . . to my astonishment [I] saw the young Cuckoo, though so newly hatched, in the act of turning out the young Hedge-sparrow. The mode of accomplishing this was very curious. The little animal, with the assistance of its rump and wings, contrived to get the bird upon its back, and making a lodgement for the burden by elevating its elbows, clambered backwards with it up the side of the nest till it reached the top, where, resting for a moment, it threw off its load with a jerk, and quite disengaged it from the nest. It remained in this situation a short time, feeling about with the extremities of its wings, as if to be convinced whether the business was properly executed, and then dropped into the nest again. With these (the extremities of its wings) I have often seen it examine, as it were, an egg and nestling before it began its operations; and the nice sensibility which these parts appeared to possess seemed sufficiently to compensate the want of sight, which as yet it was destitute of.
>
> I afterwards put in an egg, and this, by a similar process, was conveyed to the edge of the nest and thrown out. These experiments I have since repeated several times in different nests, and have always found the young Cuckoo disposed to act in the same manner. In climbing up the nest, it sometimes drops its burden, and thus is foiled in its endeavours;

> but, after a little respite, the work is resumed, and goes on almost incessantly till it is effected.
>
> . . . The singularity of its shape is well adapted to these purposes; for, different from other newly hatched birds, its back from the scapulae downwards is very broad, with a considerable depression in the middle. This depression seems formed by nature for the design of giving a more secure lodgement to the egg of the Hedge-sparrow, or its young one, when the young Cuckoo is employed in removing either of them from the nest.

These observations were met with widespread disbelief, and perhaps Sir Joseph Banks, the President of the Royal Society, also had his doubts, because Jenner's paper was initially rejected with the comment: 'Council thought it best to give you full scope for altering it.' However, Jenner stuck to his story, and he was subsequently vindicated by respected ornithologists of the day, including John Blackwall (1824) and George Montagu (1831).

Even so, 100 years later many thought Jenner's account to be 'preposterous'. Some believed that the eviction of the host eggs and young must be a passive process, that they were simply squeezed out of the nest as the cuckoo chick grew. Others persisted in the belief that it was the female cuckoo who returned to the host nest to do the evictions. For example, in his otherwise admirable account about cuckoos, August Baldamus (1892) wrote: 'The female cuckoo removes and hides the eggs of the nurse after the young parasite is hatched.'

There is no evidence, however, that adult cuckoos ever give their chicks a helping hand, and in his paper Jenner had been meticulous in excluding this possibility. First, he noticed that the same evictions of host eggs and young occurred in nests late in the summer, where cuckoo chicks hatched after all the adult cuckoos had departed. Secondly, he performed two experiments at hedge sparrow nests while adult cuckoos were still at large.

In one experiment, he found a newly hatched cuckoo chick alone in a hedge sparrow nest with a recently ejected hedge sparrow egg entangled in the nest material on the rim of the nest. The shell was cracked, and the hedge sparrow chick was still alive inside the egg and just about to hatch. He restored the egg to the nest and then returned a few minutes later to find it once more lodged on the nest rim. He saved it again and put it back in the nest but this time he removed the cuckoo chick. The hedge sparrow chick hatched a quarter of an hour later and three hours afterwards it was still being tended by its parents. Jenner then popped the cuckoo chick back in the nest; a few minutes later he checked again, and the young sparrow had been 'tumbled out' for the third time.

In a second experiment, Jenner found another young cuckoo 'that had been hatched by a Hedge-sparrow about four hours'. He then 'confined [it] in the nest in such a manner that it could not possibly turn out the young Hedge-sparrows which were hatched at the same time, though it was almost incessantly making attempts to effect it.' It's not clear how Jenner confined the young cuckoo; perhaps he tied its legs to the bottom of the nest. But the result was that the young hedge sparrows remained in the nest, alongside the cuckoo, and for the next four days the 'old birds fed the whole alike, and appeared in every respect to pay the same attention to their own young as to the young Cuckoo.'

Jenner's careful experiments and his wonderful description should have left no doubt. Incredible though it may seem, the newly hatched cuckoo chick, still naked and blind, does all the work in evicting the host's eggs and chicks, and so takes sole command of the nest. The cuckoo chick's performance has been filmed many times now, but every time I watch it, on screen or in nature, I am still amazed. What makes it all the more extraordinary is that the evictions often take place while the host parent is sitting , so the cuckoo has to push the host aside as it works its way up the edge of the nest with its load on its back. The host then does nothing to interfere as its own eggs and chicks are tossed aside, as it witnesses the destruction of its own chances of reproduction that summer.

The ejection of the host eggs, and of any host young, may begin just 8–10 hours after the cuckoo chick hatches. On Wicken Fen, cuckoo chicks have often emptied a reed warbler's nest within 24 hours of hatching. However, in a study in the Czech Republic, ejections from reed warbler nests did not begin until cuckoo chicks were on average 40 hours old, so sometimes the cuckoo might need some meals first to help build up its strength. In the nests of small hosts, such as warblers and pipits, it may take as little as 20 seconds to eject an egg, once the cuckoo has the egg on its back, but the average is three to four minutes. The cuckoo rests between each load, so three to four hours may be needed to evict the whole clutch, and sometimes as much as one to three days if the cuckoo is ejecting large host young. There is one report of an unusually late-hatching cuckoo in a dunnock nest, where a two-day old cuckoo chick evicted a seven-day old host chick. The cuckoo's performance is not without its own hazards. It often teeters on the rim of the nest, feeling with its wing stumps to make sure its load has gone; in two out of 114 ejections from reed warbler nests observed by Ian Wyllie in the fens, the cuckoo chick itself fell out of the nest.

The cuckoo chick's instinct to eject host eggs and chicks is so strong that it will not tolerate anything in the nest. If you place a small pebble or a lump of mud alongside it, it will immediately balance these on its back and eject them overboard. Once, I kept a cuckoo chick in an artificial nest for a short while, to record its begging calls in the laboratory. I put a thermistor probe next to the cuckoo, so I could monitor its temperature to make sure that it was warm enough. The cuckoo immediately objected to this pampering, and my recordings were suddenly interrupted by a loud clattering noise as the thermistor probe was heaved out of the nest and fell onto the floor below.

The urge to eject disappears by four days of age. By this time, the cuckoo usually has the nest to itself and any remaining young are likely to get crushed or will simply starve, unnoticed by their parents, underneath the rapidly growing cuckoo. In one remarkable case, however, a cuckoo chick hatched a day after a brood of four robins and, after spending a whole day trying to evict them, gave up. The cuckoo left the nest after 20 days, its normal nestling period, while, amazingly, the slow-growing robins underneath survived too and fledged at 23 days of age, 10 days later than usual.

Common cuckoo eggs hatch after an unusually short incubation period. On average, the cuckoo's egg needs just 11 days of host incubation, compared with 12 days for reed warbler eggs, 12–13 days for dunnock eggs, and 13 days for meadow pipit eggs. Therefore, provided the female common cuckoo gets her timing right, and parasitises the host nest during the laying period, before incubation has begun, her egg will hatch a day or so before the host eggs. This gives the cuckoo chick plenty of time to eject the host eggs before they hatch, likely to be an easier task than ejecting struggling host young.

How does the cuckoo egg hatch so early? The cuckoo's unusually small egg certainly reduces incubation time, but nevertheless it is often a little larger than the host eggs and still hatches a day earlier than expected from its egg mass. How, then does it hatch first? The answer is that the cuckoo's egg already has a day's head start in development when it is laid, because of internal incubation inside the female cuckoo's oviduct. This suggestion was first made by George Montagu in his *Ornithological Dictionary* of 1802, but not demonstrated for certain until 2011, when Tim Birkhead and his colleagues examined the embryos of newly laid cuckoo eggs under a microscope. Female cuckoos lay on alternate days, and ovulation occurs 48 hours before an egg is laid. It takes just 24 hours for an egg to be fully formed, from ovulation and fertilisation to the laying down of the shell. So the female cuckoo then carries the hard egg in her oviduct for an additional 24 hours before it is laid. This extra day of internal incubation gives the cuckoo chick its head start, enabling it to hatch before the host eggs. In fact, the extra 24 hours inside the female's body results in a 30-hour advantage in hatching time, because her internal temperature is 40 degrees Celsius, whereas the incubation temperature is 36–37 degrees.

At first, this seems to be yet another amazing cuckoo trick. However, many non-parasitic cuckoos also lay on alternate days, so this may be the ancestral state for parasitic cuckoos, and not a specially evolved trick for parasitism. Laying on alternate days could have other advantages too, for example giving more time to form energy reserves for eggs. For parasitic cuckoos, it also allows more time to find suitable host nests. Once a bird lays eggs at two-day intervals, then internal incubation will be the inevitable consequence if a fully formed egg spends an extra day inside the female's warm body. For example, feral pigeons lay at two-day intervals and their eggs also have embryos at a similar advanced stage of development to those of common cuckoos. Nevertheless, although neither laying on alternate days nor internal incubation are specific adaptations for parasitism, the cuckoo's head start in development is put to good use in enabling it to hatch first and eject host eggs.

In *The Origin of Species*, Darwin points out how his theory of evolution by natural selection could be refuted:

> If it could be demonstrated that any complex organ existed, which could not possibly have been formed by numerous, successive, slight modifications, my theory would absolutely break down.

This criterion applies equally to any complex behaviour pattern, such as the parasitic habits of the common cuckoo. Could the remarkable eviction by cuckoo chicks really have evolved gradually, step by step?

We have already seen evidence for gradual evolution in the egg arms race. Before they were parasitised, hosts had no defences; then host egg defences and cuckoo egg mimicry evolved gradually together. What could have been the starting point for what Darwin himself referred to as that 'strange and odious instinct', namely the cuckoo's eviction of its nest mates? If parasitism has evolved from parental ancestry, then there must be precursors of the cuckoo chick's murderous intentions already present in normal family life.

Indeed there are, shocking though this may seem. Recent observations have shattered the old cosy view of animal families. A familiar sight in the nests of most species of birds is that of chicks jostling, trying to outreach their siblings when their parents bring food. If food is scarce, younger chicks fail to compete with their larger siblings, and starve to death. However, it is now known that older chicks sometimes hasten the demise of their younger sibs, by pecking them or pushing them out of the nest. For example, in kittiwake colonies it is not uncommon for the younger chicks to be pushed out of more than half the nests, crashing to the rocks below. Young egrets and boobies are also regularly pecked and evicted from the nest by their older siblings. Once out of the nest, they are ignored by their parents and die from cold and starvation.

In species where parents raise their own young, stronger chicks normally restrain their aggression and selfishness provided there is enough food to go round. This makes good sense, because younger nest mates will be siblings, which share copies of the same genes. A common cuckoo chick, by contrast, has no genetic stake in the other young in the nest, so unrestrained selfishness is not penalised. Natural selection has had an easy job. The raw material for cuckoo selfishness is already there as part of normal family life. All that has happened is that the occasional, optional killing of nest mates, depending on food availability, has evolved into certain killing, every time.

The way common cuckoos dispose of the host eggs and chicks may seem cruel. But this host death, by chilling or drowning, is a painless one compared with that suffered by hosts of another brood parasite in Africa. The honeyguides comprise 17 species in the family Indicatoridae. They are small, inconspicuous birds of forest and open woodland, and one species, the greater honeyguide, is famous for guiding humans to bees' nests, which is the source of the family name. However there is a darker side to their apparently sweet nature: all species of honeyguide that have been studied have cuckoo-like habits. The greater honeyguide is the best known. It parasitises hole-nesting species, such as hoopoes and bee-eaters. Just like the common cuckoo, the female greater honeyguide lays one egg per host nest. The newly hatched honeyguide chick is born with ready-made weapons, sharp hooks on the tips of both the upper and lower parts of its bill. It had long been assumed that it must use these hooks to kill the host chicks, because the young honeyguide is always raised alone and dead host chicks, with stab wounds, had been found alongside it in the nest. But the killing takes place in the darkness of a nest burrow and, until recently, it had never been witnessed.

In 2012, Claire Spottiswoode and Jeroen Koorevaar published their observations from filming the killing for the first time, using infrared cameras placed inside the nests of little bee-eaters, the main host of the greater honeyguide in southern Zambia. The little bee-eaters often nest inside deep subterranean burrows dug by aardvarks. The nest chamber is at the end of a narrow tunnel, about half a metre long, which the bee-eaters excavate themselves as an offshoot of the burrow, some 30–50 centimetres below the soil surface. The field craft involved in obtaining the films combined Claire's brilliance as a field biologist with the skills of the local farm workers, who were used to digging into the hard ground for rat nests which provided 'relish', a meaty treat to go with their staple diet of maize meal. A long grass stem was inserted into the bee-eater's tunnel and its length measured when it would go no further, having reached the nest chamber at the end. The grass was then laid on the ground above the tunnel to mark the correct distance, and a shaft was dug carefully down to the nest below using a mattock.

Often, the digging team were disappointed, because only 30 per cent of the nests were parasitised by a honeyguide. Sometimes they were too late, and found a young honeyguide already surrounded by the corpses of the bee-eater chicks. Once they were greeted by a black mamba snake, whose bite is fatal for humans. But at five nests they got their timing right, and found a newly hatched honeyguide chick with host eggs just about to hatch. They placed the camera at the end of the nest chamber, with cables leading to a digital recorder at the surface, covered the roof of the shaft with a slab cut from a nearby termite mound, sealed it in with elephant dung, and then paid local children to remain on guard to ensure the equipment was not stolen.

The paper describing the films, entitled 'A stab in the dark', is as chilling as any horror story. The young honeyguide usually hatches several days before the host chicks, but its eyes still haven't opened and the burrow is in total darkness, so it is a blind assassin, and its attacks are made entirely by feel. Indeed, it will attack a human hand and has such a strong jaw that it can hang from a finger by grasping with its bill tips. Host chicks are attacked soon after they hatch. The honeyguide grabs a host chick using its bill tip, then repeatedly bites and shakes its victim for up to four minutes at a time. The bites rarely cause open wounds, but lead to haemorrhaging under the skin and heavy bruising. The host chicks make no attempt to avoid attacks and soon cease begging for food. From the time of the first attack, they take from nine minutes to over seven hours to die. The bee-eater parents are unable to see the horror in the darkness and do nothing to interfere; the films show them offering food to the honeyguide chick even as it grasps and shakes their own chicks to death.

Perhaps honeyguide chicks get rid of the host chicks by stabbing them rather than by ejecting them, because ejection would

The newly hatched chick of the greater honeyguide has sharp hooks on the tip of its beak.

The honeyguide chick uses the sharp hooks to stab the little bee-eater host chicks to death. Both photographs taken by Claire Spottiswoode, in Zambia.

be difficult from a deep nest in a hole or burrow. But what could be the precursors of bill hooks? Amazingly, even these weapons have been found in two parental species, a bee-eater and a kingfisher, where chicks will attack and kill their siblings if food is short. Their bill hooks are shorter than those of a honeyguide chick and are on the upper mandible only. Once again, the extreme adaptations of a parasite have evolved by natural selection simply exaggerating precursors in normal family life.

We now return to Wicken Fen and a newly hatched common cuckoo chick in a reed warbler nest. Its skin is bright pink; its gape is orange; and it has no spots on its tongue. The reed warbler's own chicks are smaller; they have black skin; their gapes are yellow; and their tongues have two prominent black spots. Differences in size, colour and spotting are the cues that reed warblers use to reject eggs unlike their own. Surely they should now use these same cues to reject the cuckoo chick. But they don't. Why?

One possibility is that hosts rarely get the chance to compare the cuckoo chick with their own chicks, because the cuckoo ejects the host's eggs before they hatch. But when a cuckoo hatches late, and there are now host chicks for comparison, the host still fails to reject the cuckoo, and never intervenes even as the cuckoo ejects its own chicks.

Mike Brooke and I gave reed warblers another chance to compare their own young with a cuckoo chick by experiment. We tied a second nest next to their nest, supported by a bamboo cane. Pairs that were feeding a brood of their own young were given a young cuckoo in the nest alongside, while pairs that were feeding a cuckoo were given a brood of young reed warblers in the adjacent nest. We watched for an hour and then exchanged the contents of the two nests and watched for another hour, to test whether any preferences were for a particular nest or for particular contents. Reed warblers are remarkably tolerant of experimental manipulations at their nests, perhaps because they are so used to changes in their nest surrounds as reeds grow or are blown by the wind. So the parents quickly returned and resumed feeding the young. They perched above the two nests, peered down at the two sets of chicks and then fed whichever were begging the most. There was no overall preference for either nest or for either set of contents. These experiments show that hosts will feed a cuckoo even when they have their own chicks alongside for comparison.

Richard Dawkins and John Krebs have suggested that whereas the cuckoo relies on deception to get its egg accepted, it relies on a different trick at the chick stage, namely manipulation. They proposed that the hosts may not be able to resist a cuckoo chick any more than 'the junkie can resist his fix'. This idea itself is beguiling, and almost begs to be believed. However, we found that reed warblers readily accepted chicks of other species too, raising them alongside their own despite their odd appearance. For example, reed warblers accepted a single dunnock chick in among their own brood. Dunnock chicks, like cuckoo chicks, have pink skin and an orange gape, quite unlike the black skin and yellow gapes of reed warbler chicks. Other cuckoo hosts that reject odd eggs will also accept odd chicks.

These experiments suggest that the drug analogy is incorrect. The cuckoo chick doesn't need any special stimuli to induce acceptance. Hosts of the common cuckoo simply fail to reject chicks unlike their own and will feed any begging mouth in their nest. This explains why the cuckoo chick doesn't have to mimic the appearance of the host chicks. But we are still left with the puzzle: why do common cuckoo hosts reject odd eggs but not odd chicks?

One possibility is that it is much better for hosts to reject earlier on, at the egg stage. If they eject the cuckoo egg then they save the rest of their clutch, their only unrecoverable loss being the egg that the female cuckoo removed when she laid. Even if they deserted a parasitised clutch, provided it was not too late in the season they might still have the chance to raise a replacement clutch, and with luck that might escape the cuckoo. Later rejection, at the chick stage, is less beneficial on both counts: the cuckoo chick is likely to have already destroyed the clutch, and by the chick stage there is less time for a replacement clutch that season.

Nevertheless, reed warblers on Wicken Fen are fooled by 80 per cent of cuckoo eggs. Surely a second line of defence at the chick stage would be beneficial, even if this simply saved three weeks' hard work feeding a cuckoo nestling, followed by another two weeks feeding it as a fledgling.

A second consideration is that recognising a foreign chick might be more difficult than recognising a foreign egg. An egg looks exactly the same throughout incubation, whereas a chick changes dramatically as it grows. Reed warbler chicks are naked and black when they hatch, but then a few days later they become brown as their feathers emerge. Furthermore, because host chicks often hatch over a period of a day or two, there will be young of different ages in the nest, and so considerable variation in size and appearance even within the host's own brood. To spot a stranger amongst this variation might not be easy.

This argument is also not very convincing. There are still some simple rules that hosts could use. For example, any reed warbler that only fed chicks with tongue spots would never be fooled into raising a young cuckoo.

In 1993, Arnon Lotem suggested an ingenious solution for why hosts of common cuckoos might always be doomed to accept a foreign chick. How would hosts come to recognise their own young? The answer is likely to involve learning, just as with egg recognition. We have already seen that learning works well at the egg stage. Occasionally the host is unlucky and is parasitised during the laying of its first clutch, in which case it learns both its own eggs and the foreign egg as part of its own set. But this cost of mis-imprinting is not too bad; although in future these individuals will be fooled into also accepting the foreign egg type, in many cases they will not be parasitised and so can happily raise their own young.

However, now imagine what would happen if hosts of the common cuckoo adopted this same learning procedure for chicks. If they were unlucky, and were parasitised in their first clutch, they would see only a cuckoo chick. Now the cost of mis-imprinting is much greater. If the hosts imprinted on the cuckoo chick, then they would reject their own young in any future, unparasitised nests. It turns out that it would be better not to imprint on chicks at all, but simply to accept any chick in the nest. And that is exactly what hosts of the common cuckoo seem to do. So the hosts end up accepting cuckoo chicks that look nothing like their own young.

Good ideas can come at strange times: Arnon tells me that he suddenly thought of this explanation one evening while he was waiting in line at the entrance of a cinema. For 10 years I thought this must be why common cuckoo chicks did not have to mimic the host chicks. However, beautiful theories can be refuted by new observations. Since 2003, studies in Australia have shown that cuckoo hosts can escape any potential trap of mis-imprinting. They reject chicks unlike their own, and their cuckoos have responded by evolving chick mimicry, namely chicks which look and sound just like the host's own young.

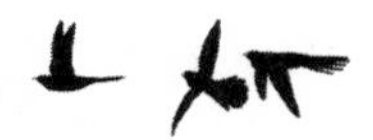

Just as common cuckoos are heralds of spring in Eurasia, so the incessant spring calling of cuckoos is familiar in Australia, and for Aboriginal people a signal of the *Ngawu*, the season for hunting eggs (September to October). An Australian aboriginal legend tells how, during the Dreamtime, Byamee, the Creator, made all the birds and then taught them how to build nests, when to lay their eggs, and how to care for their young. All the birds obeyed Byamee except for the cuckoos, who simply wanted to sing. According to the legend, the other birds complained about the cuckoos' lazy ways and chased them to the far north. From that time on, the cuckoos have always lived in the north, but every spring they return south to lay their eggs in other birds' nests. So the cuckoos have continued to spend their time singing, and every year their young fly north too, guided by the Dreamtime memories. The legend explains both the cuckoo's parasitic habits and its seasonal migration.

In Australia, there are 10 species of parasitic cuckoos. Among these are three species of bronze-cuckoos, small, sparrow-sized cuckoos with iridescent green or bronze plumage and barred underneath. Young bronze-cuckoos behave exactly like young common cuckoos; they hatch first and eject the host's eggs. However, in striking contrast to common cuckoo chicks, newly hatched bronze-cuckoo chicks look just like their host's young:

Little bronze-cuckoo chicks have black skin, like the chicks of their gerygone hosts (Australian warblers);
Shining bronze-cuckoos have yellow skin, like the chicks of their thornbill hosts; and
Horsfield's bronze-cuckoos have pinkish skin, like the chicks of their fairy-wren hosts.

These cuckoo chicks match their respective host chicks in mouth colour and downy feathering, too. The cuckoo's begging calls also sound like those of their host's chicks. Have host defences at the chick stage led to an escalation of the arms race to produce chick mimicry by these cuckoos?

Naomi Langmore, from the Australian National University, Canberra, and Becky Kilner, from Cambridge University, were the first to show that bronze-cuckoo hosts do indeed reject chicks that differ from their own. They studied the superb fairy-wren (and superb it is – the iridescent blue plumage of the male is dazzling), which is the major host of Horsfield's bronze-cuckoos in the parkland around Canberra. These cuckoo chicks have begging calls just like fairy-wren chicks and they look similar, too, with pink skin like the fairy-wrens' own chicks, though their rump is greyer. Nevertheless, the fairy-wrens deserted 40 per cent of the cuckoo chicks within a few days of hatching. The fairy-wrens were also occasionally parasitised by the shining bronze-cuckoo, whose chicks have yellow skin and different begging calls; these cuckoo chicks were always deserted. This suggests that the hosts used visual and vocal cues to reject chicks unlike their own.

Naomi and Becky discovered that the female fairy-wren was always the first to desert a cuckoo chick. Once she had made her decision, she began to build a new nest nearby. However, sometimes the decision appeared to be a difficult one; she would fly to the nest, sit in front of it staring at the cuckoo for several minutes,

RICHARD NICOLL

Two male cuckoos fighting, high over Lakenheath Fen. Male cuckoos arrive a week or two before the females and set up territories in areas where their hosts are likely to nest.

RICHARD NICOLL

Male cuckoo in flight, Wicken Fen. With long, pointed wings, a long tail and barring underneath, the cuckoo looks rather like a bird of prey.

Harbinger of spring; only male cuckoos call 'cuckoo'. The bill is opened for 'cuck', then closed for 'oo'. The drooping wings and raised tail are characteristic of a calling male.

The female cuckoo is more secretive and with good reason; if hosts are alerted to her presence near their nest they are more likely to reject the cuckoo's egg. Females come in two plumage types: grey (*left*), and rufous (*right*) which makes them harder to recognise.

A female cuckoo laying an egg in a reed warbler nest, a favourite host in marshland. First she removes a host egg, and while holding it in her beak, lays directly into the nest.

The cuckoo's egg (*middle, left-hand side*) is a little larger than the reed warbler's eggs but is a good match in colour and markings.

Sometimes hosts, such as this great reed warbler, reject the cuckoo egg by puncturing it and ejecting it from the nest.

A young cuckoo chick, still naked and blind, balances each reed warbler egg on its back, and heaves them out of the nest, one by one.

An early-hatched reed warbler chick in this nest suffers the same fate.

A reed warbler feeding a brood of four nine-day-old reed warblers (*left*) and a nine-day-old cuckoo chick (*right*). The cuckoo will need as much food as a whole brood of reed warblers.

A reed warbler feeding a seventeen-day-old cuckoo chick. It left the nest two days later.

KEITA TANAKA

A nestling Horsfield's hawk-cuckoo in Japan, exposing a false gape – a yellow wing patch – next to its own yellow gape. This tricks the host, a blue-and-white flycatcher, into bringing more food.

CHARLES TYLER

Meadow pipit, a favourite host in moorland, feeding a fledgling cuckoo. The cuckoo has now grown to six times the weight of its foster parent.

CHARLES TYLER

A meadow pipit mobbing a male cuckoo, an extraordinary contrast to its willingness to feed a fledgling cuckoo of similar size.

CHARLES TYLER

Cuckoo egg (*top left*) in a meadow pipit nest. This cuckoo race lays brown eggs, which mimic the pipit's eggs.

W.B.CARR

JUHA HAIKOLA

A cuckoo egg (*left, top*) in a dunnock nest, a favourite British host in woodland. Dunnocks accept eggs unlike their own, so this cuckoo race has not had to evolve a mimetic egg. By contrast (*right*), in Finland, another host with blue eggs, the redstart, rejects eggs unlike its own and this cuckoo race has evolved a matching blue egg (*top right*).

CLAIRE SPOTTISWOODE

The outer circle shows the variety of eggs laid by tawny-flanked prinias (an African warbler) in Zambia. Individual differences in colour and markings act as signatures by which each female can recognise her own eggs. The cuckoo finch has evolved a range of forgeries to match (*inner circle*). Each egg shown is from a different female.

then fly off to feed, only to return immediately to stare again. One female did this for a while, then flew off and started to collect cobwebs to build a new nest, but then she flew back and resumed care for the cuckoo after all, and proceeded to rear it to independence. Male fairy-wrens were sometimes a bit slow to realise what was going on and continued to feed the cuckoo for several hours, or even another day or two, after the female had deserted. But once the female began to solicit copulations for a new clutch, the male quickly turned his attention to her and abandoned the cuckoo too.

Careful observations were needed to discover these desertions, because once the cuckoo chick had been abandoned the nest was rapidly invaded by meat ants, which began to eat the cuckoo chick even while it was still alive. After a few hours, there were no remains of their feast. So if the nest had not been checked until the following day, all the observers would have seen would have been a clean and empty nest, such as is typical of predation by a snake.

Fairy-wrens that had accepted a Horsfield's bronze-cuckoo nestling in one breeding attempt did not then subsequently abandon their own young in later nests, so they clearly avoided any mis-imprinting problem. Furthermore, with more experience of their own young, fairy-wrens were more likely to reject a cuckoo. This suggests that learning is involved in chick recognition, but there must be some predisposition to focus on cues that guarantee hosts learn their own chicks. It is still not known what these cues are.

Gerygone hosts of little bronze-cuckoos also sometimes reject cuckoo chicks, despite the good match in appearance to their own young. Their method of rejecting a cuckoo chick is dramatic: they pick it up in their bill and, while it is still struggling, toss it out of the nest.

If these Australian hosts can reject cuckoo chicks, why don't common cuckoo hosts do so? One possibility is that the arms race between Australian cuckoos and their hosts is a more ancient one, so there has been more time for evolution. From similarities in their DNA, it is estimated that the common ancestor of three races of common cuckoo in the UK (those specialising on meadow pipits, reed warblers and dunnocks) dates back to around 80,000 years ago. By comparison, the Australian bronze-cuckoos are much older species, and likely to have experienced interactions with their hosts for several million years. This might have given time for evolution to proceed beyond an egg arms race to defences and trickery at the chick stage.

There is another good reason for why the arms race has escalated to the chick stage in these Australian hosts. It's that the bronze-cuckoos seem to have defeated these hosts at the egg stage. Superb fairy-wrens build untidy domed nests of grass, well hidden in low vegetation. Their eggs are pinkish-white and finely speckled with reddish-brown. The nest has a large hole as a side entrance, and although it is sometimes possible to see the eggs inside, their markings are not as clearly visible as in an open cup nest. The egg of the Horsfield's bronze-cuckoo is an excellent match of the fairy-wren's eggs in both colour and size. Naomi Langmore and Becky Kilner found that fairy-wrens never ejected cuckoo eggs, though they did abandon the clutch if they saw a cuckoo at their nest. It seems likely that their ability to recognise a highly mimetic cuckoo egg is compromised by the dark interior of their domed nest. If the hosts know they have been parasitised, but are unsure which egg is the cuckoo egg, the best thing to do is to desert and start a new nest.

Remarkably, long before these scientific studies, Aboriginal people already knew that superb fairy-wrens (Ter ter) did not reject Horsfield's bronze-cuckoo (Woor) eggs, a wonderful testament to their deep knowledge of the natural world. According to their legend, it is against bird law to reject eggs. Science has now explained why this bird law has evolved.

Thornbills and gerygones have even darker domed nests, and their respective bronze-cuckoos (the shining bronze-cuckoo and little bronze-cuckoo) have another remarkable trick which has helped beat these hosts at the egg stage. The hosts have white, speckled eggs, typical for species with dark nests. White eggs must be easier to see, which will help the hosts turn them during incubation, to check for signs of hatching, and to remove empty shells from the nest. By sharp contrast, shining bronze and little bronze-cuckoos lay plain, dark olive-brown eggs, which are very hard to see in the dark nest interior. Even researchers looking out for cuckoo eggs with the help of a torch often miss them, and only realise that a nest has been parasitised when they feel an extra egg with their fingertips. The cuckoo eggs are unusual because the brown pigment is thickly slathered on the outer surface, rather than inside the shell matrix, and it can be rubbed off with a damp cloth. These dark eggs seem to have defeated the hosts, because neither thornbills nor gerygones reject cuckoo eggs. Once beaten at the egg stage, because they can't pick out either mimetic or cryptic cuckoo eggs in their dark, domed nests, these Australian hosts might have evolved chick defences instead.

There is one other factor, too, that might help to explain why common cuckoo hosts in temperate Eurasia do not reject cuckoo chicks, namely that they are in more of a hurry to reproduce, so cannot afford to be as particular at the chick stage as Australian hosts. Only 50 per cent of adult reed warblers survive to the next breeding season, so for half of them there is just one short summer in which to raise young. As we have seen, it pays them to defend their nests against female cuckoos and to look out for odd eggs in their nests, because this protects their own eggs from destruction. But by the time the chicks hatch, it's getting late in the season and the chances of another attempt are diminishing. At this late stage, therefore, it might be best simply to work hard to care for whatever is begging in their nest. In Australia, fairy-wrens and thornbills are much longer-lived, with 70 to 80 per cent of adults surviving to the next breeding season. For them, it might pay to be cautious even late in the breeding cycle, when the chicks have hatched, because they have a good chance that they will survive to breed again the following year, when they may be more certain there isn't a cuckoo chick in the nest.

10

Begging tricks

A reed warbler feeding its brood of five young, now 7 days old.
Wicken Fen, 22 June 2014.

To sit quietly in the reeds on Wicken Fen, and watch a pair of reed warblers feeding their nestlings, is to experience another world.

The best way to do this is to tie some reeds and make a narrow channel, so the nest can be observed from the bank. Once you are sitting low down, you sense the sights and sounds from a parent reed warbler's perspective: a dense green forest of vertical reed stems and long lance-like leaves, the occasional bright flash of a yellow hoverfly, a metallic red beetle or an azure blue damselfly, the glow of white and yellow from water lilies floating in the water below, the gentle whine and hum of insects in the still air, a sudden splash from a pike, the cluck of a moorhen swimming by, the squeal of a water rail, or the shadow of a marsh harrier passing overhead. You feel the reed warbler's urgency, as it collects prey for its hungry chicks, and then broods them from time to time to keep them warm, all the while remaining alert to signs of danger amongst the background sounds, the swishing of the reeds and the loud cracks of the old reed stems drying in the sun. When you have become immersed in this intimate and hidden world for a few hours, it's a shock to stand and be exposed once more to a human's view of the fen, with huge skies and distant horizons.

When reed warblers on Wicken Fen have a cuckoo chick in their nest, they behave as if nothing was amiss; they feed and protect it just as if they were caring for a brood of their own chicks. They bring the same food: mainly bill-fulls of small flies or single large items, such as caterpillars, moths, butterflies, damselflies, hoverflies or dungflies. They also bring food at about the same rate to a cuckoo chick as they do to an average brood of four young reed warblers of the same age. The only difference is that the cuckoo is dependent for longer, 17–20 days in the nest plus 16 days after fledging, compared with just 11 days as nestlings plus 12 days as fledglings for a brood of host young.

In a study in the Czech Republic, Tomáš Grim, from Palacký University, found that reed warblers deserted 16 per cent of cuckoo nestlings when they were about 15 days old, when the normal nestling period expected for a brood of their own young had clearly been exceeded. However, this response is unlikely to be an evolved defence against cuckoos, because he found that a similar percentage of reed warbler broods was also deserted when the normal nesting period was prolonged experimentally, by replacing a brood with younger chicks from another nest. The occasional desertion of a cuckoo chick, therefore, was probably a by-product of the reed warblers protecting themselves from continuing to feed slow-growing broods of their own, which are likely to fail.

On Wicken Fen, by contrast, we have never recorded reed warblers deserting cuckoo chicks, despite their prolonged nestling period. How, then, does a single cuckoo chick persuade its reed warbler foster parents to work as hard as they would for a whole brood of their own young? Rebecca Kilner, David Noble and I spent two summers trying to solve this question by various experiments.

First, we wondered if the cuckoo's bright orange gape was the key attraction for the hosts. This is certainly the case for rufous bush chats, a favourite host of the common cuckoo in southern Spain. Fernando Alvarez, from the Biological Station of the Coto Doñana, used non-toxic food dyes to colour the normally yellow gapes of nestling rufous bush chats bright orange. Their parents immediately brought them more food! So for these hosts, the cuckoo nestling's orange gape works as a 'super-stimulus', producing a greater response than the gape colour that the parents normally expect. Reed warbler nestlings also have yellow gapes. However, when we used food dye to make them orange, the parent reed warblers did not bring more food, nor did they prefer an orange-gaped chick in among a brood of chicks with yellow gapes. So, for reed warblers, an orange gape does not work as a super-stimulus.

Next, we thought that the hosts might be stimulated simply by the cuckoo chick's large size. If so, then a large chick of another species should be provisioned just like a cuckoo. We tested this by an experiment, done under licence, where we temporarily replaced a brood of reed warblers with a single blackbird chick, just for a few hours. (Meanwhile, we kept the reed warbler brood warm and well fed in an artificial nest.) We predicted that if the parent reed warblers' provisioning was determined by the size of the chick in their nest, then they should bring as much food to a single blackbird as to a single cuckoo of the same weight.

Reed warblers have their chicks rather late in the summer, in June and July, by which time most blackbirds have finished breeding, so it was hard work finding blackbird broods from which we could borrow a chick for our experiment. A further practical problem was that at first this experiment didn't work because the blackbird chick crouched in the reed warbler's nest and would not beg. We then realised why: the blackbird was used to a stable nest in a bush, not one that swayed in the wind. So we anchored the nest, by tying the supporting reeds to a bamboo cane in the mud. Once the nest was made steady, the blackbird chick began to beg beautifully, and the reed warblers immediately responded by feeding it. However, the results of this experiment at several nests showed that the blackbird was fed at a much lower rate than a cuckoo chick of the same weight. (At the end of these experiments, of course, the blackbird chicks were returned to their rightful nests and the reed warblers were given back their own broods. Their parents continued to care for them as if nothing usual had occurred, unaware of the contribution to science their offspring had made.)

Clearly, the cuckoo's large size is not a sufficient stimulus on its own to persuade the reed warblers to bring it enough food. Then we realised that parents don't simply look at their chicks, they listen to them too. When a reed warbler chick begs for food, its call is a high-pitched '*tsi . . . . . . tsi*'. When a cuckoo begs, its call is much more rapid: '*tsi. . tsi. . tsi. . tsi*'. In fact, to our ears, the cuckoo didn't sound like a single chick; it sounded more like a whole brood of hungry chicks. Was this vocal trick the one that spurred the hosts into treating it like a brood of host young?

We tested this by repeating the experiment with a single blackbird chick in a reed warbler nest, but this time the blackbird was given a helping hand. We placed a little loud speaker next to the nest; whenever the blackbird begged, we broadcast cuckoo begging calls through the speaker. The reed warblers reacted quickly to the extra begging cries and became much more active in collecting food. We did this experiment at several nests, and the results were clear: with the extra stimulation from cuckoo begging calls, the hosts now brought as much food to the blackbird as they did to a cuckoo of the same weight. In further experiments, we found that broadcasts of the calls of a brood of reed warblers had the same stimulating effect. So the cuckoo's exuberant calling, which sounded like a hungry brood of host young, was indeed the key. An important finding was that the blackbird chick itself did not beg more in response to our broadcast, so it was certainly the calls that spurred the reed warblers on to working harder.

We discovered later that we were not the first to come up with this idea, although we were the first to test it. In 1743, a book was published whose German title is translated as *Winged Theology: an attempt to inspire humankind to admiration, love and reverence for their creator by a closer consideration of birds.* The author, J. H. Zorn, had certainly considered cuckoos closely. He wrote:

> The young cuckoo cries as loud as a whole brood of host nestlings. The reason is to enhance the feeding by the foster parents.

He had beaten us by more than 250 years!

In an essay written in 1926, the mathematician and philosopher Alfred North Whitehead suggested that the guiding motto of every natural philosopher should be 'Seek simplicity and distrust it.' How wonderful it was to think that the cuckoo tricked the hosts with visual mimicry in eggs and vocal mimicry with chicks! But this explanation is too simple. At a week of age, the cuckoo chick's begging call does indeed match the calling rate of a week-old brood of four reed warbler chicks. But as the cuckoo gets older, its calling rate increases still further: by two weeks, the rate is equivalent to two broods of reed warblers. Yet it is still fed like one brood of four young.

Why does the cuckoo have to call faster and faster as it grows? It was Becky Kilner who realised that the way the cuckoo chick's call works is both more subtle and more interesting than by simple vocal mimicry of a brood. When reed warblers provision a brood of their own young, they respond both to a visual cue – the total area of begging mouths on view, and to a vocal cue – the begging call rate of the brood. The visual cue gives the parents a rough guide to how much food to bring, because it is related to chick number (more chicks, more mouths) and chick age (older chicks, larger mouths). The vocal cue enables parents to fine-tune their provisioning in relation to chick hunger (hungrier chicks call more rapidly). So if reed warblers have more chicks, or older chicks, they work harder, and if they hear their chicks calling more rapidly, they work harder still.

How does the cuckoo chick exploit this system? The young cuckoo needs as much food as four young reed warblers. Its problem is that it presents just one begging mouth. A cuckoo chick's mouth is, of course, much larger than the mouth of one reed warbler chick. But it is smaller than the total mouth area of four reed warbler chicks, which is the visual stimulus that the hosts use to calibrate the demands of four young reed warblers. As the chicks get older and increase in size, the cuckoo chick's visual stimulus, a single mouth, becomes relatively even smaller in comparison with the four mouths of a host brood of the same age. The cuckoo's trick is to compensate for its increasingly deficient visual stimulus by boosting its vocal signal. At a week of age, calling at the same rate as a brood of four reed warblers is sufficient, but at two weeks it needs to sound like eight hungry chicks to persuade the hosts to bring enough food.

So the cuckoo chick's begging trick is a subtle one: it has 'tuned in' to the way the hosts integrate visual and vocal cues when they raise a brood of their own young. Nestling honeyguides, which use their bill hooks to kill the host young, also sound like several chicks, so rapid begging calls may be a regular trick in parasitic birds that are raised singly.

Sometimes nature's inventiveness is truly astonishing. In Japan, Keita Tanaka and Keisuke Ueda, from Rikkyo University, Tokyo, discovered that the Horsfield's hawk-cuckoo has an equivalent trick, but it exaggerates the visual component of the begging display. The young cuckoo has a yellow patch of skin under each wing, the same colour as its yellow gape. When the hosts (blue-and-white flycatchers) come with food, the cuckoo usually exposes one wing patch beside its mouth, which makes it appear as if there are two hungry mouths in the nest, rather than one. If it's very hungry, it exposes both wing patches, so there now appear to be three hungry mouths! Sometimes, the hosts offer food to a wing patch. When Tanaka and Ueda blackened the wing patches, they found that the hosts then brought less food. Perhaps this cuckoo uses visual trickery, to look like several chicks, rather than vocal trickery, to sound like several chicks, because the host nests are particularly vulnerable to predators that locate nests by sound.

It might seem surprising that parent birds are fooled by such simple vocal and visual signals, when a closer look would surely reveal a cuckoo, not a brood of their own young. We might pride ourselves that we would never be tricked so easily. But we are manipulated in the same way by advertisements every day. My favourite example comes from an experiment done by Melissa Bateson and her colleagues in a coffee room at Newcastle University, where there was an honesty box for payment of drinks. Above the box, there was a notice reminding everyone to pay. In alternate weeks, an image was added above the notice: either some flowers or a pair of eyes. On average, people paid three times as much for their drinks when eyes were displayed. Remarkably, this was an unconscious response, because during debriefing at the end of the experiment, most said that they had never noticed the images. Eye images on notices can also be effective in reducing litter and bike thefts.

I sometimes imagine having a conversation with my reed warblers on the fen. 'Why don't you realise that there's a cuckoo chick in your nest?' I ask them. 'We don't see the world like that,' they reply. 'We just respond to begging mouths and calls.' Then the reed warblers ask me: 'Why don't you realise that no one is really watching you? Those are just pictures of eyes.' Just like the reed warblers, we often rely on fast, unconscious responses to make decisions, so we, too, are susceptible to manipulation by simple cues.

Persuading the hosts to bring enough food is only one of the cuckoo's problems. It also has to contend with predators, such as jays and magpies, and sometimes mammalian predators, such as weasels. Most nestlings crouch when a predator approaches, in the hope that they will not be noticed. By contrast, the common cuckoo nestling has some remarkable defences from about a week of age. If you put your hand towards it, it erects its head feathers and opens its orange gape. Then it suddenly rears up and snaps down again. This is a shock even for someone familiar with the performance, and must surely be an effective deterrent against predators.

Edward Jenner provided a good description in his cuckoo paper from 1788:

> Long before it leaves the nest, it frequently, when irritated, assumes the manner of a bird of prey, looks ferocious, throws itself back, and pecks at any thing presented to it with great vehemence, often at the same time making a chuckling noise like a young hawk. Sometimes, when disturbed in a

> smaller degree, it makes a kind of hissing noise, accompanied by a heaving motion of the whole body.

Perhaps the cuckoo's orange gape makes the display even more effective. In addition, if touched, the cuckoo produces foul-smelling brown liquid faeces. These are quite unlike the normal faeces, which are white and contained in a gelatinous sac, which makes it easier for the hosts to carry them away.

Why has the cuckoo chick evolved these remarkable defences? One reason is surely the cuckoo's unusually long nestling period, which will increase the chance that predators will find it. Young reed warblers leave the nest well before they can fly, clinging to the reeds with their strong feet. This suggests that a reed warbler's nest is a vulnerable place to be, and should be escaped as soon as possible. But the cuckoo has to stay for longer, simply because it takes more time for a larger body to grow. The second reason is that the cuckoo's loud and rapid begging calls are likely to attract predators to the nest. Certainly, the calls often led us to discover parasitised nests that we had missed at the egg stage. We now encounter another wonderful adaptation of cuckoo chicks which mitigates the costs of their exuberant begging calls.

When a predator approaches a nest, parent birds give alarm calls to warn their chicks of danger. These calls tend to vary between species; for example reed warblers give a low-pitched '*churr*', while dunnocks give a higher-pitched '*tseep*'. Our experiments reveal that young nestlings respond only to the alarm calls of their own species. Thus, reed warbler chicks cease begging and crouch in the nest when reed warbler '*churr*' calls are broadcast to them, but they carry on begging if dunnock '*tseep*' calls are broadcast. Dunnock chicks do the reverse: they respond to '*tseep*' but not to '*churr*'.

This specific response is not simply an outcome of experience, because when nestlings are cross-fostered to be raised by another species they do not tune in to their foster species' alarms, but still retain a selective response to their own species' alarms. This suggests that newly hatched nestlings already have their brains pre-tuned to their own species' signals. This enables them to pick out their parents' alarms against a background of irrelevant sounds (for example, the calls of other species or noises from vegetation). It also means they can respond appropriately the first time danger threatens. A correct first response might save their lives.

On Wicken Fen, when reed warblers have a cuckoo chick in their nest, they give '*churr*' alarm calls in exactly the same way as when they are protecting a brood of their own, which is further evidence that they do not recognise the impostor. My colleagues, Joah Madden and Stuart Butchart, and I tested how cuckoo chicks responded to these alarms by presenting them with broadcasts of recordings. As with the reed warblers' own chicks, we found that cuckoos raised in reed warbler nests tuned in specifically to reed warbler '*churr*' alarms, and ignored the alarms of other species. In response to '*churr*' alarms, not only did they cease begging calls, they also opened their orange gapes wide, a preparation for defence.

How do cuckoo chicks become so specific in their response? To test if learning might be involved, we cross-fostered some newly hatched cuckoos from reed warbler nests to the nests of dunnocks or robins, and then tested their alarm responses when they were six days old. Remarkably, they had not tuned in to the different alarm calls of these new foster parents, but still had a specific response to reed warbler '*churrs*'. This suggests that the race of cuckoo that specialises on reed warblers is pre-tuned to reed warbler alarms, just like the hosts' own chicks. Pre-tuning might be essential so that the cuckoo responds correctly the first time an alarm is heard. Continued begging when a predator is nearby might be fatal; the cuckoo's first mistake might be its last. So this cuckoo race has both well-matched eggs and well-tuned chicks. Further studies are needed to test other cuckoo races.

The common cuckoo's need for special begging tricks is the result of a problem of its own making. By ejecting all the host eggs and young from the nest, it is guaranteed every meal that arrives. But this benefit comes at a price: the cuckoo now has to do all the work of soliciting food from its foster parents. Some other cuckoo species have the opposite problem: the cuckoo chick tolerates the host young and so gets their help in stimulating the host parents to bring food to the nest, but now the cuckoo has to compete with the host chicks once the food arrives.

The problem of how a cuckoo competes with the host chicks has been particularly well studied in great spotted cuckoos in southern Spain, where the main host is the magpie. This species of cuckoo does not eject the host eggs or chicks, so it is raised in a brood alongside magpie young. The begging cries of several chicks in the nest stimulate the magpie parents to bring more food than they would to a cuckoo on its own. The cuckoo then takes advantage of the extra food with two tricks that persuade the magpie hosts to give it an unfair share.

The first trick, discovered by Manuel Soler and colleagues from the University of Granada, is that the cuckoo chick has white papillae on the roof of the mouth, which the hosts find particularly alluring. The second trick, discovered by Tomas Redondo and colleagues from the Biology Station of the Coto

Doñana Reserve, is that the cuckoo chick exaggerates its begging calls to sound like a particularly hungry chick. A magpie chick gradually increases its begging intensity as it gets hungrier, with more frenzied gaping and more rapid calling. By contrast, a cuckoo calls with maximum intensity even when it has just been stuffed full of food. As a result, the cuckoo gets the most food, grows to be the largest chick in the nest, and yet still persists with its famished cries. This begging performance was so disturbing for a visitor to Redondo's laboratory that she insisted he fed the 'poor starving' cuckoo every few minutes, until she realised she was being deceived.

Why should magpie parents favour a large and seemingly still hungry chick? In fact this makes good sense in normal circumstances, when the nest is not parasitised. Magpies adjust their brood size in relation to the food available by allowing the smallest nestlings to die if food is scarce. They feed the largest nestling first, and only when this is satiated does the next-largest get fed. If food is in short supply, the smallest chicks then quickly die and the magpies raise a few healthy young. This is much better than spreading scarce food out evenly, which would produce a large brood of weedy chicks, none of whom might survive.

The great spotted cuckoo chick's exuberant begging exploits this system, which works so well for the magpies in unparasitised nests. Faced with a stimulus of a large chick which never seems to get satiated, the magpie hosts are tricked into diverting most of their hard-won food to the cuckoo, even while their own young perish alongside.

11

Choosing hosts

Male cuckoo, mobbed by a pair of meadow pipits.
Holme, North Norfolk, May 2014.

Gilbert White's *The Natural History and Antiquities of Selborne*, the Hampshire village where he was born, died and served as parish priest, has been continuously in print ever since its first publication in 1789. With over 200 new editions and translations, it is reputed to be the fourth most published book in the English language, after the Bible, the works of Shakespeare and John Bunyan's *The Pilgrim's Progress*.

The book is a compilation of letters to his friends, Thomas Pennant, the leading zoologist of the day, and Daines Barrington, a barrister, explorer and naturalist. In these letters, White provides a precise and often affectionate account of his daily observations on the weather, fauna and flora of the parish. While other naturalists were travelling abroad to collect their specimens, often by shooting them, White never ventured further than Derbyshire and, as his biographer Richard Mabey comments, 'was so overcome by the size of the Sussex Downs that he referred to them as a vast range of mountains'.

Rather than collecting and describing dead specimens, Gilbert White took his notebook outside to make field observations of living animals and plants, and in doing so became Britain's first ecologist. He wrote:

> Faunists are too apt to acquiesce in bare descriptions, and a few synonyms: the reason is plain; because all that may be done at home in a man's study, but the investigation of the life and conversation of animals, is a concern of much more

> trouble and difficulty, and is not to be attained but by the active and inquisitive, and by those that reside much in the country.

In the preface to his book, he recommended that 'stationary men [should] pay a more ready attention to the wonders of the Creation, too frequently overlooked as common occurrences,' and concluded that 'these his pursuits, by keeping the body and mind employed, have, under Providence, contributed to much health and cheerfulness of spirits, even to old age.' Gilbert White spent some 60 years of his life in Selborne village. He was born in the vicarage on 18 July 1720, and died 100 metres away in 'The Wakes' on 26 June 1793. His letters demonstrate that a wonderful way to observe the changing natural world is indeed simply to stay in one place.

The Natural History of Selborne makes frequent reference to cuckoos. In Letter IV to Daines Barrington, written on 19 February 1770, Gilbert White muses on how the cuckoo chooses its hosts:

> Your observation that 'the cuckoo does not deposit its egg indiscriminately in the nest of the first bird that comes in its way, but probably looks out a nurse in some degree congenerous, with whom to intrust its young' is perfectly new to me; and struck me so forcibly, that I naturally fell into a train of thought that led me to consider whether the fact was so, and what reason there was for it. When I came to recollect and inquire, I could not find that any cuckoo had ever been seen in these parts, except in the nest of the wagtail, the hedge-sparrow [dunnock], the titlark [meadow/tree pipit – White did not distinguish these], the white-throat, and the red-breast [robin], all soft-billed

> insectivorous birds . . . This proceeding of the cuckoo . . . is such a monstrous outrage on maternal affection, one of the first dictates of nature, and such a violence on instinct, that, had it only been related of a bird in the Brazils, or Peru, it would never have merited our belief. But yet, should it farther appear that this simple bird, when divested of the natural maternal instincts . . . may be still endued with a more enlarged faculty of discerning what species are suitable and congenerous nursing-mothers for its disregarded eggs and young, and may deposit them only under their care, this would be adding wonder to wonder.

Writing just a few years later in his famous cuckoo paper, Edward Jenner (1788) also commented on the cuckoo's selectivity, noting the hedge-sparrow (dunnock), water-wagtail (pied wagtail) and titlark (meadow/tree pipit) as the three main hosts. He watched a pair of titlarks feeding a young cuckoo in their nest and, 'as it is a bird less familiar than many . . . to satisfy myself that they were really Titlarks, [I] shot them both, and found them to be so.' Jenner suggested that the cuckoo chose small birds as hosts, partly because small birds are more abundant, so there would be more nests available to parasitise, but also because in the nest of a larger host 'the young cuckoo would probably find an insurmountable difficulty in solely possessing the nest, as its exertions would be unequal to the labour of turning out the young birds.'

Recent studies have confirmed Jenner's suggestion that the cuckoo chooses host species that are abundant. In Britain, the three current favourite hosts are among the commonest species in their respective habitats: there are races of cuckoo specialising on reed warblers in marshland, meadow pipits in moorland, and dunnocks in farmland and scrubland. Other regular British hosts are the robin and pied wagtail, also fairly abundant species. However, the cuckoo avoids other potential host species, which are also common, have accessible nests and a suitable diet for raising young cuckoos. Why not use them too?

For example, in farmland and scrub, blackbirds are usually more abundant than dunnocks and robins. Why isn't there a cuckoo race specialising on blackbirds? Tomáš Grim and his colleagues tackled this question by field experiments in the Czech Republic and Hungary. They took newly hatched cuckoo chicks from reed warbler or great reed warbler nests and placed them, singly, in blackbird nests with eggs. The cuckoo chicks quickly ejected the blackbird eggs, so they had no problem ejecting a larger egg from a larger nest than normal. However, the blackbird parents were reluctant to feed a cuckoo, and none survived beyond a few days. This was not a case of rejecting a lone chick, because blackbirds happily raised a single blackbird chick.

The researchers then tested cuckoo chicks cross-fostered to song thrush nests, another potential host that cuckoos do not use. Surprisingly, the cuckoo's problems here were of a different kind. The cuckoo chick was unable to eject the thrush's eggs, mainly because a thrush nest is deeper and has steeper sides than a blackbird nest, but also because, unlike blackbird nests, song thrush nests are lined with mud and the cuckoo's legs kept slipping on the hard, smooth surface. Experiments showed that cuckoos also failed to eject reed warbler eggs from song thrush nests, so the problem was the steep and slippery nest walls, not the large egg. However, if the researchers gave the cuckoo a helping hand, by removing the thrush's eggs, they found that it was fed very well by the thrushes and grew even better than in reed warbler nests. So a diet of mainly worms, with some snails, is fine for raising a young cuckoo. Finally, cuckoo chicks were placed together with a brood of song thrush chicks, but now they fared poorly in competition with host young and none of them survived to fledging.

These experiments suggest cuckoos avoid blackbirds, simply because blackbirds won't feed them. It's not yet known why this is so. Blackbirds feed their young mainly on worms, and this diet was fine for cuckoos raised in song thrush nests. So the problem is not one of diet. Perhaps the cuckoo's begging signals are not appropriate for blackbird foster parents? Cuckoos avoid song thrushes for a different reason: the young cuckoo would be raised successfully if it was the only chick in the nest, but it cannot eject the host eggs from such a steep and slippery-sided nest and doesn't survive in competition with the host young.

What about other potential hosts that cuckoos usually avoid? Experimental 'parasitism' of their nests with model cuckoo eggs reveals that some of these are very strong rejecters of eggs unlike their own. This applies, for example, to reed buntings, blackcaps, tree pipits, chaffinches, spotted flycatchers and willow warblers. Many of these species are even stronger egg rejecters than the cuckoo's favourite hosts. How did they evolve such strong rejection? We have already seen that species which have never engaged in an arms race with cuckoos, because of an unsuitable diet or an inaccessible nest, are acceptors of eggs unlike their own. This suggests that strong rejection of eggs must have evolved in response to past parasitism by cuckoos. So they are likely to be old hosts, which still bear the scars of the arms race their ancestors ran long ago, just as we have wisdom teeth and an appendix, signs of our ancestry.

If this interpretation is correct, we are left with the question: why did these cuckoo races go extinct? One possibility is that their hosts won the arms race, evolving such good egg signatures and such good egg rejection that their cuckoos couldn't keep up with successful forgeries. The other possibility is that their cuckoo races went extinct for ecological reasons. Perhaps these hosts were more abundant in the past, and a decline in their density meant that they were no longer profitable as a cuckoo host. In this case, no matter how well a cuckoo race was adapted to its host, it would be doomed to extinction as its niche faded away. Now that these hosts are no longer parasitised, their egg signatures might fade and they may lose their egg rejection behaviour, too. If so, they will become available once more as suitable cuckoo victims, and the arms race might be repeated all over again.

This brings us to a question that is still unresolved: how do the various races of the common cuckoo, each with a particular egg type suited to its host species, remain distinct? The most likely explanation has been discussed ever since the days of Edgar Chance, namely that a female cuckoo inherits her egg type genetically, and then she comes to choose to parasitise the same host species that raised her, by learning its features when she is a nestling or fledgling. For example, a young female cuckoo raised by reed warblers would imprint on the characteristics of her foster parents and then, when adult, would choose to parasitise reed warblers. The green egg laid by her mother obviously fooled her reed warbler foster parents: she is the living proof of this. So, if she inherits this same green egg type and chooses reed warblers in turn, then the match between cuckoo and host eggs will be maintained across the generations.

We still do not know whether egg colour and pattern is inherited in cuckoos, but it is in other species of birds, so this seems very likely to be true. Neither do we know whether cuckoos imprint on their hosts. Edgar Chance himself tried to determine whether a female cuckoo victimised the same host species that raised her as a youngster. In 1923, he collected 17 cuckoo eggs or newly hatched cuckoo chicks from the vicinity of Pound Green Common, and placed them into the nests of meadow pipits, stonechats or skylarks. He ringed the nine that survived to fledge in the hope that some would return to the Common to breed, but none was seen again. In the 1970s, Ian Wyllie ringed a large number of cuckoo nestlings raised in reed warbler nests in the fens, but again none returned to his study site to breed. In 1987 and 1988, Mike Brooke and I tried a different technique, raising cuckoos in captivity with either robins or reed warblers as hosts. However, when we tested these cuckoos as adults they showed no propensity to breed, so we could not determine whether they had imprinted on their host species. A lot of hard work produced no results whatsoever!

In another captive study, Yvonne Teuschl and Barbara and Michael Taborsky, from the University of Vienna, hand-raised cuckoos in one of five different 'habitats' (these were cages containing objects of different colours and shapes). When the cuckoos were tested as adults, a year or two later, both males and females preferred their familiar habitat when given a choice. This suggests that habitat imprinting might increase the chance that a cuckoo encounters the host species that raised it. However, even within the same habitat there are likely to be several potential host species, so imprinting on the hosts themselves (their appearance, songs and calls, or nests) would be necessary to refine host choice to one species.

Although there is still no direct evidence for host imprinting in cuckoos, recent experiments have shown that it does occur in another brood-parasitic bird. In Africa, there are 19 species of finches in the genus *Vidua*, and they are all brood parasites, laying their eggs in the nests of grassfinches (Estrildidae). These hosts are remarkable for the striking mouth patterns of their chicks, which vary between species. Each *Vidua* parasite species specialises on one estrildid host species. The parasite chick is raised alongside the host young and shows remarkable mimicry of the host chicks' mouth pattern.

The village indigobird, widespread in sub-Saharan Africa, has been particularly well studied. It is a little smaller than a sparrow; the males have a glossy blue-black plumage and the females are streaky brown. It lays its eggs in the nests of just one host species, the red-billed firefinch. If you look in a red-billed firefinch nest, it is difficult to pick out the parasite chick because it looks exactly like a host chick. The host young have bright orange gapes, with extraordinary white swellings and blue spots on the edge of the mouth, and black spots on the roof of the gape. These patterns are specific to red-billed firefinches and are as striking as any signatures you will see on an egg. The indigobird chick mimics this complex mouth pattern to perfection. Robert Payne and his colleagues from the University of Michigan tested how red-billed firefinches would respond to chicks with different mouth patterns by cross-fostering chicks of other species into their nests. The firefinches were more reluctant to feed chicks with mismatching mouths, so the indigobird's mouth mimicry is important in ensuring it gets fed properly alongside the host young.

Therefore, a female village indigobird has to ensure she parasitises only red-billed firefinches, the one host for whom her chick has a matching mouth. It's also important that she mates with a male of her own species, to ensure her offspring have the correct mouth pattern. If she mated with another species of indigobird, her hybrid offspring might have a different mouth pattern, and so her chicks would not survive so well. Her choice of mate is not as straightforward as in many other birds, because there are several indigobird species which look very alike. How does the female village indigobird solve these problems of host choice and mate choice?

In aviary experiments, Robert Payne and colleagues cross-fostered eggs so that some indigobirds were raised by Bengalese finches, a domestic form of an Asian finch, the white-rumped munia, which, of course, indigobirds would never encounter in the wild. Others were cross-fostered to be raised by their normal red-billed firefinch hosts. When these nestling indigobirds became adults they were given a choice of hosts in an aviary with a mixture of breeding species. Female indigobirds that had been raised by red-billed firefinches chose to parasitise the nests of red-billed firefinches, while females raised by Bengalese finches chose Bengalese finches as hosts. This is a beautiful confirmation that a female parasite's host choice occurs through imprinting on the host species that raised her.

However, the story is even more intriguing. Male indigobirds play no part in choosing which nest to parasitise, but their experience as a nestling also colours their future behaviour because they copy the songs of the host species that raised them; male indigobirds raised by red-billed firefinches sing red-billed firefinch songs, while those raised by Bengalese finches sing Bengalese finch songs. So when a male indigobird sings, he announces the identity of the host species that raised him!

Female indigobirds do not sing, but they nevertheless imprint on their host's songs and prefer to mate with a male indigobird which sings that same song. Therefore, a female indigobird ensures she mates with a male raised by the same host species that raised her, so host imprinting determines both her host choice and her mate choice. The result is that female and male indigobird lineages remain faithful to the one host species, and their mouth mimicry is maintained across the generations.

It would be wonderful to perform such cross-fostering experiments with cuckoos, but they are much more difficult to keep in captivity than finches. When Mike Brooke and I sought advice from Miriam Rothschild, who had hand-reared cuckoos in the 1960s, she warned us that they would be tricky to keep. In fact, she suggested we abandon all hope of studying host imprinting and instead used cuckoos as a model for schizophrenia! When they are being hand-fed by humans, or fed by hosts, she told us, cuckoos are remarkably tame and unperturbed by the events around them. However, once they become independent, she warned us, they change character within a few hours and become wild and easily disturbed. Perhaps we should have heeded her advice; it would have saved a fruitless experiment.

The alternative way to test for host imprinting is by field experiments. Some young cuckoos from reed warbler nests, for example, could be transferred to the nests of sedge warblers. The prediction would be that these young would imprint on the wrong host species and, when they returned the next year to breed, would choose to parasitise sedge warbler nests. There would be the problem of finding these cross-fostered young the following summer, because although young cuckoos tend to return to the general area where they were born, they often breed 10 to 20 kilometres away. Now satellite tracking of birds has become feasible, it should be possible to follow young cuckoos by tagging them just before they fledge but, even so, large samples would be needed because of heavy mortality of young before they return to breed.

My guess is that cuckoos do imprint on their hosts, just like parasitic finches, and that this explains how the cuckoo races remain distinct. Although there is no direct evidence for host imprinting, we do know that individual female cuckoos are usually remarkably host-specific when they lay their eggs. We have already seen evidence for this from Edgar Chance's study on Pound Green Common, where Cuckoo A and her successors favoured meadow pipits, almost exclusively, even though there were other potential hosts in the same habitat. Chance also collected a series of nine eggs one summer from a female cuckoo which specialised on spotted flycatchers, and another of 14 eggs from a female who specialised on yellowhammers. These two unusual hosts are sparsely distributed, and both female cuckoos must have ignored many other host species in their territory.

Recent studies also show remarkable female host fidelity even within the same habitat. In two marshland sites in the Czech Republic, Marcel Honza and colleagues from the Academy of Sciences, Brno, followed female cuckoos by a combination of radio-tracking, to determine where they laid their eggs, and DNA profiles to determine maternity of cuckoo nestlings. This is a particularly valuable study because at one site there were three, and at the other four, very similar host species, all warblers in the same genus (*Acrocephalus*), and all breeding in close proximity within a female cuckoo's territory. Indeed an individual female cuckoo could potentially watch all three or four host species from the same vantage point. Nevertheless, seven of the nine females targeted just one host species: two females specialised on reed warblers; one specialised on great reed warblers; three specialised on marsh warblers; and one specialised on sedge warblers. Such fine host specialisation within one marshland habitat strongly suggests female cuckoo are imprinted on their host species.

Along the Chikuma River, in the suburbs of Nagano City, central Japan, female cuckoos were likewise host-specific. DNA profiles were used to assign maternity for 98 cuckoo nestlings, a combination of a truly heroic field effort by Hiroshi Nakamura and expertise in the laboratory by Karen Marchetti and Lisle Gibbs, of McMaster University, Canada. Twenty-two of the 24 female cuckoos at the study site parasitised the nests of just one host species. Sixteen females specialised on great reed warblers, and six specialised on azure-winged magpies.

There is good evidence, therefore, that individual female cuckoos target one particular host species, even when very similar hosts are available. This suggests that female cuckoos are imprinted on the characteristics of one host. Now, what are male cuckoos up to? After a century of speculation, the picture is still confused.

One possibility is that a male cuckoo mates with any female he encounters, whatever her host preference. In the Chikuma River study, DNA profiles were used to assess paternity; seven out of 19 males (37 per cent) had offspring in the nests of more than one host, and so must have mated with females who were targeting different host species. Genetic analysis of cuckoos in lowland Britain also suggests that a male cuckoo often mates with females who have different host preferences. But now we have a problem: how could the distinctive egg types of the various races be maintained in the face of cross-mating by male cuckoos?

The answer is that, at least in theory, egg type might be under female genetic control, a suggestion made in 1933, back in the days of Edgar Chance, by R. C. Punnett, Professor of Genetics at Cambridge. This is a possibility in birds because of their mode of sex determination. In both birds and mammals, the sex of an offspring is determined by which sex chromosomes it inherits. In mammals, females have two X chromosomes (XX), so all their egg-cells have an X chromosome, while males have one X and one Y (XY), so their sperm have either an X or a Y chromosome. Therefore offspring sex is determined by the father: if an egg (X) is fertilised by a Y sperm it produces a son (XY), if it is fertilised by an X sperm it produces a daughter (XX).

In birds, it is the other way round: the female has two types of sex chromosome (WZ), so her egg-cells have either a W or a Z chromosome. The male has two Z chromosomes (ZZ), so all his sperm have a Z chromosome. So now it is the female who determines the sex of the offspring. Egg-cells with a W sex chromosome, on fertilisation, produce daughters (WZ), while those with a Z sex chromosome, on fertilisation, produce sons (ZZ). If egg colour was determined by genes on the W chromosome, then daughters would always lay the same type of egg as their mother. Not all the genes influencing egg colour need be on the W chromosome. Most could be on other chromosomes, inherited from either parent, with the mother's W chromosome genes determining which of these other genes get 'turned on': those making green eggs for the reed warbler race, those making brown eggs for the meadow pipit race, and so on.

In this scenario, only female cuckoos would be in separate races, and a male could mate with females from any race because he has no influence on his daughters' egg type. Indeed, cross-mating by males would maintain the cuckoo as the one species. This would explain very neatly why all the races of the common cuckoo look the same. There are no differences in appearance, for example, between cuckoos specialising on reed warblers and meadow pipits. They differ only in the colour of eggs they lay.

The inheritance of egg colour and pattern in cuckoos has still not been studied. However, in other bird species genes from both the mother and the father have equal influence on egg colour. This is true, for example, in the village weaverbird in Africa, where we have seen that the remarkable variation in egg colour and spotting acts as signatures, enabling individuals to recognise their own eggs. If, as in other species, genes from both parents influence egg colour, not only would a female cuckoo have to remain faithful to the host species that reared her, she would also have to restrict her matings to male cuckoos raised by the same host as she was, otherwise the egg mimicry would break down in the next generation. In this scenario, the different races of the cuckoo would be genetically isolated, just like different species.

A recent study in northwest Bulgaria, by Frode Fossøy and colleagues from the Centre for Advanced Study, Oslo, has revealed that cuckoo races can indeed sometimes be genetically isolated, even when they live side by side in the same small area. They studied the DNA of cuckoo nestlings raised by three hosts: marsh warblers, which bred in herbaceous vegetation, great reed warblers, which bred in reed beds, and corn buntings, which bred in bushy grassland. These three habitats were distributed in a patchy mosaic within an area of some 10 square kilometres, so here cuckoos that parasitised the three hosts would certainly all wander over the same geographic area. Nevertheless, there were clear genetic differences between cuckoos raised by the three hosts, showing that in this area, despite intermingling, matings must usually be between female and male cuckoos raised by the same host species.

How could a female recognise a male from her own race? One possibility is there might be subtle differences in voice. Gilbert White himself pioneered the idea that differences in voice could be as characteristic of a species as differences in appearance. He was the first to realise that there were three species of willow-wrens in Britain, though in appearance they all look rather alike. These are the little, yellow-green warblers now classified in the genus *Phylloscopus* ('leaf seekers'), which flit through the summer foliage catching small insects. On 17 August 1768 (letter XIX to Thomas Pennant in *The Natural History of Selborne*), White wrote:

> I have now, past dispute, made out three distinct species of the willow-wrens, which constantly and invariably use distinct notes . . . I have specimens of the three sorts now lying before me; and can discern that there are three gradations of sizes, and that the least has black legs [chiff-chaff], and the other two flesh-coloured ones [willow warbler and wood warbler]. The yellowest bird is considerably the largest . . . and makes a sibilous grasshopper-like noise [this is the wood warbler] . . . Ray . . . [the] great ornithologist, never suspected that there were three species.

Three years later, in Letter X to Daines Barrington, written on 1 August 1771, Gilbert White notes that although they have a simple two-note call, '*cuck-oo*', individual male cuckoos can also sometimes be distinguished by their voice:

> A neighbour of mine, who is said to have a nice ear . . . finds upon trial that the note of the cuckoo (of which we have but one species) varies in different individuals; for, about Selborne wood, he found they were mostly in D: he heard two sing together, the one in D, the other in D sharp, who made a disagreeable concert . . . and about Wolmer-forest some [sing] in C.

Could there be subtle differences in voice between cuckoos of the different races? So far, there has been just one study to investigate this, by Tibor Fuisz, from the Hungarian Natural History Museum in Budapest, and Selvino de Kort, from Leiden University, the Netherlands. They recorded the calls of 142 male cuckoos in Hungary in two habitats: forests, where the main host is the robin, and reed beds, where the main host is the great reed warbler. To control for any geographical variation in calls, they compared adjacent pairs of forest and reed-bed habitat in three widely separated regions, at least 200 kilometres apart, in the north, the south and the east of the country. There were slight differences in calls between these three regions, mainly in call duration and the pitch of the first note '*cuck*', but the major difference was between the habitats; forest cuckoos had a markedly lower-pitched second note '*oo*' than reed-bed cuckoos.

These findings are intriguing; clearly there's more to a simple '*cuck-oo*' than we had first assumed. But it is too early to say whether this will be a 'eureka' moment, like Gilbert White's discovery that there was more than one species of willow-wren. It is possible that the call is not a sure mark of cuckoo race. Lower-pitched calls travel best through dense foliage, and individual males might learn to adjust their call to suit their habitat. Even if a male's call did signify his race, it still remains to be shown whether females choose mates based on such call differences, and whether the result is mating between male and female cuckoos raised by the same host.

Perhaps our current confusion about the exact nature of cuckoo races is because cuckoo mating behaviour varies between populations. In some areas, the races might be isolated genetically and best regarded as subspecies, perhaps in the process of evolving into different species. Over 50 years ago, in 1954, H. N. Southern, from the University of Oxford, noted that egg mimicry seemed to be best in those cuckoo races that occupied large tracts of uniform habitat, for example Hungarian reed beds (great reed warbler hosts) and Scandinavian forests (redstart hosts). Here, there would be plenty of opportunity for matings to occur between males and females of the same race. By contrast, in other areas more affected by human activities, Southern noted that egg mimicry is often poorer. He supposed that this was because the habitat was broken up into such small patches that male cuckoos more often encountered females of other races, and frequent interbreeding disrupted the egg mimicry.

In support of this idea, both studies showing that male cuckoos often mated with females of more than one race have been in areas extensively modified by humans, namely along the Chikuma River in the suburbs of Nagano City, Japan, and across lowland Britain. Perhaps, as we continue to destroy natural habitat and fragment the cuckoo's landscape still further, we are slowly eliminating the distinct cuckoo races across many parts of Europe.

How did the various cuckoo races evolve in the first place? Now we can bring together all the various studies in this chapter to suggest a likely sequence of events. Although individual female cuckoos certainly have favourite hosts, they will parasitise another species if a nest of the main host is not available. For example, Edgar Chance's cuckoos sometimes laid an egg in the nest of a skylark or yellowhammer if they failed to find a suitable meadow pipit. From their study of host clutches in museum collections, Arne Moksnes and Eivin Røskaft estimated that in 5 to 10 per cent of cases a common cuckoo egg was laid in the 'wrong' host nest. Hiroshi Nakamura's radio-tracking of females in Japan revealed a similar level of mistakes, with 8 per cent of eggs laid in the nests of alternative hosts.

Most of these eggs laid in alternative host nests will be doomed. For example, linnets feed their young on seeds and never successfully raise a cuckoo to fledging. Nevertheless, they are still occasionally parasitised, probably by desperate cuckoos which specialise on dunnocks and cannot find a suitable dunnock nest. Other cuckoo eggs will no doubt be rejected because they are a poor match for the host eggs. Once in a while, however, some of the mistakes will produce a surviving offspring. If these lucky survivors imprint on the new host species, then this will be their chosen victim when they become adult, and a new cuckoo race will be born.

Many of these new races will be short-lived, perhaps lasting for just one or two generations, because the adult cuckoos will not produce sufficient surviving offspring to maintain the race. But sometimes the new race might proliferate. At first, cuckoos specialising on the new host might do even better than those that stick to the old host. There might be less competition for the new host's nests, and the new host might also be less likely to reject cuckoo eggs, especially if it has not been exploited before. As the new race increases in numbers and the hosts begin to evolve rejection of eggs unlike their own, the stage is then set for a new cuckoo egg type, one that matches the new host. Note that in this sequence, the behavioural specialisation comes first, through imprinting, followed by the evolution of egg mimicry later on.

Hiroshi Nakamura and his colleagues have recently witnessed the birth of a new cuckoo race in central Honshu, Japan, which follows this sequence of events. Sixty years ago, the three most common cuckoo races here were those that specialised on bull-headed shrikes, great reed warblers and Siberian meadow buntings. Nowadays, these first two hosts continue to be cuckoo favourites, with 10 to 20 per cent of their nests parasitised in many areas. However, although the bunting is still abundant, it has become a rare host, with less than 1 per cent parasitism. Nakamura's experiments with model eggs show that it is the most discriminating of the three hosts, so although the cuckoo egg is often a good match, copying the little brown scribbles on the host eggs, it is possible that this race is being driven to extinction by host rejection.

In its place, a new cuckoo race is evolving, one that parasitises azure-winged magpies. These magpies have spread dramatically in recent years, particularly into areas of higher elevation, and as a consequence have come into more contact with cuckoos. The first records of parasitism were of single nests in 1956, 1965 and 1971. Since then, the magpie has become one of the cuckoo's main hosts in central Honshu. The increase in parasitism has been documented at Nobeyama Heights, an area first colonised by the magpies in 1967. From 1981 to 1983, 30 per cent of magpie nests were parasitised, but by 1988 it had reached 80 per cent, with many nests containing several cuckoo eggs. Similar rapid increases have been reported elsewhere, with 30 to 60 per cent of magpie nests parasitised by the 1980s.

This remarkable spread occurred because many female cuckoos simultaneously began to use the magpies as secondary hosts, as the magpies spread into their range. The cuckoo eggs that appeared in the magpie nests were particularly variable, reflecting their origins from all three former races. Cuckoo nestlings raised in magpie nests presumably imprinted on the new host, because Nakamura's radio-tracking shows that many female cuckoos now specialise on magpies. As a result, the new host is suffering much higher parasitism than the old hosts. In some areas almost every magpie nest is parasitised.

It seems unlikely that this situation can persist. Some local magpie populations have declined due to the heavy parasitism or have been wiped out altogether. In other areas, the magpies are fighting back, by defending their nests against female cuckoos, by ejecting cuckoo eggs, or by deserting parasitised nests. In some areas, 40 per cent of the cuckoo eggs are being rejected. This must be exerting strong selection for egg mimicry by this new cuckoo race. It will be fascinating to see if the cuckoos can evolve effective forgeries before the magpies drive them to extinction.

These observations of old host species that have apparently beaten the cuckoo, by evolving strong egg rejection, and of new hosts evolving defences, show that life as a brood parasite is not easy. Yes, cuckoos and their kind avoid the burdens of parenting and so have the potential to lay more eggs than a normal nesting bird. They may enjoy a temporary advantage when their hosts are naive. But the hosts fight back, and in the end cuckoos need a complex toolkit of trickery to succeed. Perhaps, just as full-time cheats in human society are usually caught in the end and pay a price, so host defence might limit the evolutionary success of the brood parasites, explaining why they comprise just 1 per cent of all bird species. After long days searching for host nests at a suitable stage for my model eggs, I often think that if I was a bird, building a nest and raising my own young would make for an easier life than that of a cuckoo.

12

An entangled bank

Five hobbies feasting on newly-emerged mayflies, high over the fen.

In the final paragraph of *The Origin of Species*, Charles Darwin uses the metaphor of an entangled bank to provide a poetic vision for how the diversity and ecological complexity of the natural world has resulted from natural selection:

> It is interesting to contemplate an entangled bank, clothed with many plants of many kinds, with birds singing on the bushes, with various insects flitting about, and with worms crawling through the damp earth, and to reflect that these elaborately constructed forms, so different from each other, and dependent upon each other in so complex a manner, have all been produced by laws acting around us . . . growth with reproduction; inheritance . . .; variability . . .; a ratio of increase so high as to lead to a struggle for life, and as a consequence to natural selection, entailing divergence of character and the extinction of less-improved forms. Thus from the war of nature, from famine and death . . . the production of the higher animals, directly follows. There is a grandeur in this view of life . . . from so simple a beginning endless forms most beautiful and most wonderful have been, and are being evolved.

Not everyone might regard the habits of cuckoos as 'most beautiful'. When visitors to Wicken Fen see me searching through the reeds and discover that I'm looking for cuckoo eggs, many say: 'Oh good. Are you throwing them out?' But surely everyone will agree that cuckoos are 'most wonderful', in the sense of strange, astonishing and marvellous to behold. Before Darwin, observers were full of wonder that the Creator would design a bird with no parental instincts. Today, naturalists are still full of wonder at how parasitic cuckoos have evolved from parental ancestry, and how their trickery has co-evolved with host defences.

Darwin himself expressed this continuing sense of wonder in the final pages of *The Origin*:

> When we no longer look at an organic being as a savage looks at a ship, at something wholly beyond his comprehension; when we regard every production of nature as one which has had a long history; when we contemplate every complex structure and instinct as the summing up of many contrivances, each useful to the possessor . . . how far more interesting . . . does the study of natural history become! . . . When I view all beings not as special creations, but as the lineal descendants of some few beings which lived long before the first bed of the Cambrian system was deposited, they seem to me to become ennobled.

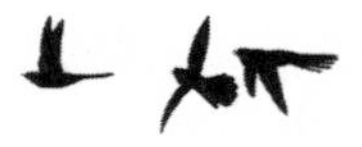

Once more, I am sitting by the Wicken Lode, the waterway that winds westwards through the centre of the reserve. Sitting on a bank seems a fitting way to contemplate Darwin's entangled bank. In the reed fringes along the edge of the lode, several reed warbler nests have been parasitised and the warblers are now unwittingly incubating a cuckoo egg, a living time bomb that will destroy their clutch. Then, as I gaze down into the still waters below, I begin to think beyond my obsessions with the world of cuckoos and their hosts.

The oil paintings of my eldest daughter, Hannah, have taught me how to see the many layers in a reflected surface. Her paintings capture a brief moment as you walk along a street and glance at café window; a dream-like world, where reflections of passers-by and smudges on the glass surface intermingle with coffee cups and lights inside the café, which seem to float beyond. There are many layers, too, as I look in the water below me: first I see the reflections of blue sky and of a flock of swifts, high above, scything the air below a billowing white cloud; then I focus on the sheen of the water surface, and bright blue damselflies resting on the lily pads; finally I look through the water, where there are shoals of fish feeding in the mud at the bottom of the lode. And I begin to realise that through all these layers – the skies above, the water surface, and the depths below – there are interactions as beautiful and wonderful as those between cuckoos and their hosts.

Gilbert White spent the best part of 60 years in his beloved village of Selborne. I have been lucky to travel the world, though I have spent the last 30 summers on Wicken Fen watching cuckoos and their hosts. But one could spend a lifetime here, just sitting on this bank, and still always be discovering something new.

We begin our celebration of an entangled bank on the water surface, where a moorhen swims along the edge of the lode towards her nest, hidden in a clump of rushes and reeds. The nest has seven eggs; four have large reddish spots at the blunt end, three are smaller with fine speckling. One might wonder if two different females have laid eggs in the same nest. Twenty years ago, David Gibbons and Sue McRae, research students at Cambridge University, discovered that moorhens in the fens do indeed often play at cuckoos, by parasitising the nests of other moorhens. They colour-ringed a population of about 80 breeding pairs at a fenland site near Peterborough, so they could follow the behaviour of individuals, and used DNA profiles to identify parasitic eggs.

Sue and David found that 10 to 20 per cent of moorhen nests were parasitised by other moorhens, often with just one foreign egg, but sometimes with up to six. Some parasitic eggs came from females on neighbouring territories, laying a few parasitic eggs before they then laid a normal clutch in their own nest. These females were trying to augment their breeding success with a few extra eggs foisted on their neighbours. Others came from females whose nests were predated during the laying of a clutch on their own territories. These females were trying to salvage the remainder of their clutch by laying eggs parasitically next door. Finally, some came from females who couldn't find space to set up a territory of their own and who were trying to get at least some success by parasitism.

This last category of females had very low breeding success, perhaps partly because they were poor-quality individuals, but also because any attempt to breed purely by parasitic laying is likely to be unrewarding for a moorhen. A cuckoo can easily survey many host territories from a concealed perch. A moorhen is clumsy and conspicuous in flight and has to walk from one territory to the next. It would find it much harder to watch hosts and to gain access to sufficient nests at the correct stage of egg laying to beat the rewards from nesting and bringing up its own young.

When a moorhen lays in another moorhen's nest, she doesn't remove a host egg, but simply adds her egg to the host clutch. Parasitic eggs that appear in an empty nest are quickly ejected or pecked and eaten by the hosts. But once the host has begun her clutch, she doesn't eject parasitic eggs. It might be difficult for a female to recognise a foreign egg, because her own eggs are often variable in colour and markings. Nevertheless, hosts often desert a nest if they are parasitised early on in laying, or if several parasitic eggs appear at once. Moorhens do not have the benefit of DNA profiles, but even the limited knowledge that 'there are more eggs here than I can have laid myself' can be a useful rule for rejection.

Moorhens lay their eggs in the evening, usually just after darkness falls. At this time, the male takes over the duties of incubation and nest defence, perhaps because he is larger than the female and better able to chase off nocturnal predators. Parasitic eggs are laid in the evening too, so this raises the possibility that the host male might copulate with the intruding female and fertilise either the parasitic eggs, or some of the eggs that she lays later in her own nest. Sue McRae's DNA profiles revealed that this never happens. All the parasitic eggs are fertilised by the parasite's mate, and he also fathers all the eggs that a parasite lays back home in her own nest. This means that both members of the host pair should try to keep parasitic females at bay.

Sue set up video cameras with image intensifiers, so she could film laying behaviour during dusk and by moonlight. During normal laying, the female arrives at her nest, stands next to it and calls softly '*puck, puck*' to her sitting mate. She has her head raised, she is relaxed, and she often preens while she waits for him to leave. He then steps aside and stands nearby while she settles on the nest. She sits there for about half an hour to lay. Then she leaves, and the male sits on the nest once more.

Parasitic laying is a remarkable contrast. The parasite's mate stays at home, so she arrives in the dark alone. Her entry to the territory is probably easiest at night, when the male is on the nest, because during the day, when the female is incubating, the male patrols the territory and is vigorous in evicting all intruders.

The parasite female charges quickly towards the nest in silence, and with her head held low. She has no hesitation and must know the exact location of the nest from previous scouting visits. Sue filmed nine parasitic layings. In one case, there were no hosts present and she laid in peace, though she was clearly nervous. In two cases, the host female was on the nest, laying her egg for the evening. She sat tight, while the parasite squeezed alongside, facing in the opposite direction and trying to protect her head from the resident female's pecks. In one of these cases, the host female called and her mate arrived to join in the attack.

In the other six cases, the host male was on the nest when the parasite female arrived. Once again, she squeezed alongside him, head to tail, and sat there quietly while his blows rained down on her. Parasites never fought back and always remained motionless. The hosts may have limited their aggression because a more violent struggle would have cracked their own eggs. Parasite females laid quickly, in two or three minutes, and then ran off back to their own territories, often pursued by the host male. These remarkable film sequences show that the parasite females need a combination of stealth, speed and bravery to succeed.

Occasional parasitic laying has now been recorded for over 200 species of birds. This 'part-time' cheating is a regular tactic for trying to produce at least some offspring when a female is prevented from nesting normally, by shortage of nest sites or territories, or because her clutch has been taken by a predator. But birds are not the only creatures to foist care of their eggs onto other parents. We now change our gaze from the water surface and peer into the depths of the lode, where one of the most abundant fish, the bitterling, has a remarkable relationship with freshwater mussels.

Bitterling are small fish, up to seven centimetres in length. In spring, the males become colourful, with red eyes, a dark violet back, a pink-red flush underneath, and a vivid green stripe along the side. They set up territories around freshwater mussels, which live half-buried in the mud at the bottom of the lode. Most territorial males defend just one mussel, but some may have several mussels in their territory. If another male approaches, he is head-butted and chased off.

Breeding females are dull coloured, grey-green on the back with silver sides, but it is easy to identify them when they are ready to spawn by their long ovipositor, a tube hanging down below that may be as long as the female's body. When a female with an extended ovipositor approaches, the male displays to her by quivering his body alongside, and then he leads her to his mussel. Mussels extract food particles and oxygen from the water by passing a stream of water over their gills. Water enters through an inhalant siphon and exits through an exhalant siphon. The female bitterling inspects the exhalant siphon, determining the suitability of the mussel by the oxygen concentration in the water passing out.

If she decides this is a suitable place to lay her eggs, then the next sequence happens with tremendous speed. She sweeps down, inserts her ovipositor deep inside the exhalant siphon, extrudes from one to six large eggs in less than a second, and then swims off. The male then immediately ejaculates sperm into the inhalant siphon, where they will be swept inside the mussel by the inflowing water to fertilise the eggs. For the next minute, the male is especially aggressive, and with good reason because neighbouring males sometimes try to sneak in to fertilise the eggs, and sometimes a whole shoal of up to 60 non-territorial males rush past and release sperm too. Both the resident male and these sneakers sometimes also compete by releasing sperm into the mussel's inhalant siphon before the female lays.

The bitterling's eggs become lodged deep in the mussel's gills, which provide a safe haven for their development. They hatch 36 hours later, then the fish embryos live on their yolk reserves for about a month, growing to one centimetre in length before emerging through the exhalant siphon into the dangerous outside world.

Some mussels are laid in repeatedly by the same or several female bitterlings, and may end up with 100 or more young bitterlings in their gills. They may suffer damage to their gills and disruption to the water flow, and the young bitterlings also compete for oxygen with the mussel's own developing larvae. In many ways, therefore, the relationship is like that between the cuckoo and its hosts. Do mussels defend themselves against bitterling parasitism? Recent studies by Martin Reichard, Carl Smith and colleagues from the University of St Andrews show that indeed they do, but defences take time to evolve, just as they do for cuckoo hosts.

In Turkey, mussels and bitterlings have lived together for at least two million years. Here mussels have strong defences: they are quick to close their exhalant siphons if stimulated by touch, which must make it difficult for the female bitterling to lay her eggs, and they often dislodge bitterling eggs and embryos by contracting their shell valves, to pass a stream of water over their gills, and then they eject them through the exhalant siphon. In central and western Europe, by contrast, including the lodes of Wicken Fen, bitterling are recent colonists, within the last 100–150 years. Here, the mussels do not have these strong defences. As with many cuckoo–host interactions, this will be a wonderful opportunity to watch evolution in action, as the mussels begin to defend themselves against the new invaders.

We remain sitting on our bank, but now we change our gaze once more, this time to the skies above. On a few warm mornings in May there is a sudden and spectacular mass emergence of thousands of mayflies from the lode. The young stages, the nymphs, are aquatic and live for a year or two, feeding on algae and vegetation. When they emerge from the water and become winged adults, they live up to their name, the Ephemeroptera, lasting but a day (*ephemeros*) on the wing (*ptera*). Adult mayflies do not feed; they live for just a few hours, during which they find a mate, lay eggs and die. They have large wings and long tails, which act as parachutes, and they shimmer as they dance and float through the air, but they are weak fliers and provide a feast for predators.

We are watching a flock of 12 hobbies swooping fast and low over the lode, enjoying this bonanza of food. These are the most agile and graceful of falcons. Their long, scythe-like wings sometimes give them the appearance of a large swift, and indeed they can catch swifts and swallows on the wing, dashing at tremendous speed to pluck one out of the skies with their talons. But in the spring hobbies often feed on insects, which they seize with their claws and then hold up to their beak to devour in flight. They hunt the mayflies with a regular beat, flying into the wind for 100 metres or so to catch prey, and then turning away from the lode and flying back downwind to repeat the circuit. By choosing the best place to sit on the bank, we can watch them speeding past and catching mayflies just a few metres away.

Richard Nicoll has spent many hours photographing the wildlife on Wicken Fen, and I have one of his superb photos, which captures the grace and precision of a hobby about to make a catch. Both hobby and mayfly are in perfect focus. The hobby's yellow feet have swung up, so the claws are held directly in front of its beak. Its long grey pointed wings are in perfect balance, so although this is a frozen moment you can sense the speed as the hobby closes in on its kill, its dark eyes intent on the floating mayfly just a few centimetres ahead.

At first, this seems a one-sided arms race, with the slow-flying mayfly no match for the accuracy and speed of a hobby, and easy prey for other predators, too. But the synchronous emergence itself provides safety in numbers and is the mayfly's key trick for defence. When all the adult mayflies emerge together, the predators enjoy a brief bonanza, but their capacity to capture prey is swamped. Individual mayflies are safest from predation during these peaks of emergence. An alternative explanation for why mayflies all emerge together is that it might enhance an individual's mating success. A neat test of this idea is possible, because some species of mayfly are parthenogenetic; these species have only females, which give virgin birth to offspring genetically identical to themselves, and so adults don't need to mate. These parthenogenetic species have exactly the same synchronous emergence as sexual species. So reducing individual predation through predator swamping is probably the major selective pressure favouring synchrony.

We could sit on the bank for a lifetime to admire countless other tricks which predators have evolved for finding and capturing their prey, and defences which their prey have evolved for concealment and escape. But arms races involve not only battles between different species: predators versus prey or parasites versus hosts. There are also intense conflicts within species: between rivals for mates, and between males who are keen to mate and females who are reluctant to do so. These also provide an intriguing part of Darwin's entangled bank.

We return our gaze to the water surface. Water striders, or pond skaters as they are sometimes called, are skating over the surface of the lode. Their legs are long and slender. The middle pair is the longest and is used for rowing, the hind pair is for steering, and the front pair, held forward, has claws for grabbing prey. They detect the ripples from struggling spiders and insects that have fallen into the water, dash over to grab and pierce them, and then suck out the juices inside.

Male water striders are also searching for mates. When a male encounters a female, he pounces on top of her and then tries to secure a mating by grasping her with elongated genitalia at the tip of his abdomen. It pays a male to try to mate even with females who have already mated, because his sperm will displace previous sperm from the stores inside the female's tract, to give him paternity of her eggs. However, a female tries to avoid superfluous matings because, with a male on her back, she is less mobile, has lower feeding success, and is more likely to be caught by a predator. The female has a weapon for resisting unwanted males: a spine on the tip of her abdomen, which she jabs up into the male as he attempts to grasp her.

There are many species of water striders. In species where the males have the most elaborate grasping genitalia, females have the longest spines. Therefore male structures to force matings have co-evolved with female structures to resist. This arms race between the sexes within a species is an exact analogy of our arms race between cuckoos and hosts, where better cuckoo trickery to deceive (egg mimicry) has co-evolved with better host resistance (egg rejection).

Other female insects try to avoid superfluous matings by deception rather than by force. In many damselflies, some females are brightly coloured, and look like males, rather than having the typical dull female colouration. Females that mimic males are less likely to be harassed by males in search of matings, and so are better able to lay their eggs in peace. This raises the question: why aren't all females brightly coloured? One possibility is that brighter individuals are more conspicuous to predators. They may be more likely to end up in the mouth of a hungry reed warbler, so the proportions of females that are bright or dull may reflect a balance of selective pressures. The other possibility is that as more and more females mimic males, the deception becomes less effective. Indeed, if all females were mimics, then clearly it would pay a male to check every bright individual closely, to determine if it was a potential mate. So the outcome of evolution might be a mixture of female guises, dull and bright females, like the mixture of grey and rufous female cuckoos that has evolved to thwart host defences.

Darwin's entangled bank is clothed with interactions every bit as strange as those between cuckoos and hosts. The 'war of nature', entailing the 'famine and death' of natural selection, has given us much beauty and wonder: from the dances of mayflies and the speed and grace of the hobby, to the guile of moorhens, water striders and damselflies, struggling to outwit their own kind. We are all familiar with climate change and with the idea that animals and plants must adapt to changes in the physical world. But even if the physical environment remained constant, evolution wouldn't come to a halt. The organic world is forever changing, and organisms will continue to evolve, simply to keep track with changes in their predators, parasites and competitors. Watching cuckoos and their hosts provides a window onto the wonders of this extraordinary entangled bank.

13

Cuckoos in decline

A female cuckoo, bubbling, pursued by three calling males. Wicken Fen, 31 May 2014.

Studying in an ancient university gives a broad perspective on one's own work and ideas in a changing world. We begin with two Fellows of my college in Cambridge, Pembroke, from five centuries ago. Nicholas Ridley was Master of Pembroke from 1540 to 1553. His portrait hangs in the college dining hall and records that he was born in 1503 and died on 16 October 1555, when he was burned at the stake as a Protestant heretic during the reign of Catholic Queen Mary. One of his crimes was to believe that the bread and wine of the Eucharist were symbolic of Christ's body and blood, not truly transubstantiated during the consecration. His was an agonising death because the fire had too many faggots and he burned slowly; during his 40-minute ordeal his fellow martyr, Bishop Latimer, called out: 'Be of good comfort, Master Ridley, and play the man; we shall this day by God's grace light such a candle in England, as I trust shall never be put out.'

One of Ridley's pupils was William Turner, who became a Fellow of Pembroke College in 1530. Turner is now recognised as the first major student of natural history in England, and he is commemorated in a stained-glass panel in Pembroke College library. His book on birds, published in 1544, identifies all the species mentioned by Pliny and Aristotle, deciphering their descriptions and matching them to the species he had seen. But he also adds his own careful observations.

Turner records 'titlings' (pipits) as a favourite host of the cuckoo:

> I have observed no other bird in life more frequently than this following the Cukkow's young and rearing it, as though its own.

He had a keen eye for behaviour, too, noting that robins and redstarts differed not only in plumage but also in voice and in the way they flicked their tails, and so he refuted Aristotle's idea that the disappearance of redstarts in the autumn came about because they were transmutated to robins. Of course, we now know that redstarts migrate to Africa for our winter.

Turner was also a pioneering botanist. His *Herbal*, published in three parts between 1551 and 1568, provides the first scientific records of over 200 of our native plants and gives an account of their 'uses and vertues'. Here are some of the 'vertues' of strawberries:

> Strawberries leaves taken in meate helpeth they that are diseased in the milt, so doth also the juice dronke wyth hony. The same is good to be given wyth pepper for them that are short winded. There is a juice pressed out of strawberries whiche by continuence of tyme encreaseth in strengthe and that is a remedy against the sores and wheales of the face and against blodshotten eyes . . . Many use this herb to . . . stoppe issues of women and to strengthen the gumes and to take away the stinking of the same.

Turner embraced Ridley's religious views, and he fled to continental Europe during Queen Mary's reign. He returned from exile when the Protestant Queen Elizabeth I ascended to the throne, and he dedicated his *Herbal* to her with fulsome praise.

Standing before these memorials to two who dared to challenge ideas of transubstantiation or transmutation brings contrasting reflections. The stained-glass tribute to William Turner makes me smile and realise how quaint my current studies of cuckoos might seem to students of future generations. Nicholas Ridley's portrait brings home darker thoughts of how difficult it is to comprehend old values in a changing world. Surely, our horror now at the treatment of Ridley will be matched by the horror of future generations at the way we treat the natural world.

According to the latest assessment by Stuart Butchart and his colleagues from BirdLife International, 1,240 species of birds (12 per cent, or one in eight, of the some 10,000 species extant today) are threatened with extinction. To this we may add another 838 species (8 per cent) classified as 'near threatened', giving a total of 2,078 species, or a fifth of the world's species, of conservation concern. There has been a steady and continuing deterioration in the status of birds in the last three decades, with even familiar common species now in serious decline. In Europe, there have been particularly marked declines in farmland species and in long-distance migrants that breed in Europe and winter in sub-Saharan Africa. The principal threat is from human activities, particularly habitat loss as forests are destroyed and wetlands are drained to provide land for the needs of our growing human population.

This decline in birds is just an indicator of a more general decline in all biodiversity. While our goals continue to be dominated by short-term economic gain, rather than long-term values, the natural world will continue to diminish. Yet recent estimates suggest that conservation is eminently affordable, if only we changed our values. The conservation of sufficient habitat to ensure the survival of the world's endangered bird species would cost some 78 billion dollars per year. This is less than 20 per cent of the annual global consumer spending on soft drinks, or less than 50 per cent of the annual bonuses paid to bankers in recent years.

The recent decline in cuckoos, our harbinger of spring, is a potent symbol of the diminishing natural world. Since the early 1980s, cuckoo numbers in the UK have declined by 65 per cent, an alarming decrease which has led to them being 'red listed' as of highest conservation concern. The causes might be complex and are not known. The greatest decline has been across lowland England and Wales. In the north of Scotland, cuckoo numbers have remained steady or even shown an increase in some areas. Calculations by the British Trust for Ornithology (BTO) show that the cuckoo decline cannot be explained by a decline in host populations. Considering the three main host species over the whole of the UK, meadow pipits have declined but reed warblers and dunnocks have increased during the last two decades.

Could host nests now be less available to cuckoos? In recent years warmer springs have led to earlier breeding in many species. Analysis across 20 sites in continental Europe reveals that the first arrival date of cuckoos advanced by an average of five days over the 40-year period from 1947 to 2007. This has kept track with the earlier spring arrival by long-distance migrant host species which, like the cuckoo, also winter in Africa south of the Sahara. However, short-distance migrant host species, which winter in North Africa or within Europe, arrive on the breeding grounds on average 15 days earlier than they did 40 years ago, so cuckoos are now arriving too late to parasitise their early nests. Over the past 20 years, short-distance migrants have become less popular as hosts, suggesting that a mismatch in breeding times caused by climate change is leading to a change in host use by cuckoos across Europe.

What about cuckoo arrivals in the UK? There are good records for the first arrival dates of the cuckoo on Wicken Fen. In the first half of the nineteenth century Leonard Jenyns, a friend of Charles Darwin, was curate and then vicar of the church in the village of Swaffham Bulbeck, just a few kilometres from Wicken. Jenyns had been offered the post of naturalist on the *Beagle* before Darwin, but had declined because of his parish duties. Gilbert White was one of his heroes, and as a schoolboy Jenyns had copied out nearly the whole of *The Natural History of Selborne* 'under the apprehension that I might never see the book again'. From 1820 to 1831, Jenyns kept meticulous records of the phenology of the flora and fauna in his parish, including the arrivals of the summer migrants. In a letter to Jenyns on 12 October 1845, Darwin praised this effort:

> My work on the species question has impressed me very forcibly with the importance of all such works . . . containing what people are pleased generally to call trifling facts . . . which make one understand the working or economy of nature.

We can compare Jenyns's first dates for the cuckoo (in italics below) with those from the past 60 years, recorded by Chris Thorne, Fellow of St Catherine's College, Cambridge, and leader of the Wicken Fen Bird Ringing Group since 1971. The average first dates are as follows, with the earliest and latest first dates for each time period in brackets:

1820–1831: 29 April (21 April; 8 May)
1947–1957: 19 April (16 April; 22 April)
1970–1979: 21 April (15 April; 28 April)

1980–1989: 21 April (14 April; 24 April)
1990–1999: 20 April (14 April; 26 April)
2000–2009: 19 April (12 April; 25 April)

These data suggest that cuckoos now arrive on Wicken Fen some 10 days earlier than in Jenyns's day, but surprisingly there has been no change during the last 60 years. Analysis of first cuckoo dates at most other sites across the UK with long-term records also shows no significant change over the past 50 years. So this contrasts with the earlier arrivals reported in continental Europe.

Nevertheless, some hosts in the UK have certainly advanced their breeding during the past few decades. For example, dunnocks and reed warblers, two of the cuckoo's favourite hosts, breed on average six days earlier now compared with the mid-1990s. However, a recent analysis by the BTO shows that any mismatch between cuckoo arrival and host breeding could have only a small effect on cuckoo populations and cannot explain the recent dramatic cuckoo decline in Britain.

A more likely problem for cuckoos in the breeding season is the severe decline in their favourite food supply, namely caterpillars of moths and butterflies. Since 1968, the Rothamsted Insect Survey has monitored annual populations of large moths across England, Wales and Scotland, with a network of about 100 light traps. In the 35 years to 2003, the annual total number of moths caught declined by 31 per cent. Considering individual moth species, populations of two-thirds of the 337 species studied have declined, half of these by 50 per cent or more. The greatest declines in moths have been in the southern half of Great Britain, in England and Wales, where the cuckoo declines have also been the most marked.

Could cuckoos also be having problems in winter? Two or three hundred years ago, there was heated debate over the autumn disappearance of cuckoos and many other of our breeding birds. It was known that bats hibernated, so it was thought that perhaps birds did too. In his poem *The Spring*, Thomas Carew (1595–1640) imagines life being awakened from winter torpor by the warmth of the sun:

> . . . the warm sun thaws the benumbed earth,
> And makes it tender; gives a sacred birth
> To the dead swallow; wakes in hollow tree
> The drowsy cuckoo, and the humble-bee.

John Ray, too, pondered on the fate of cuckoos during winter. In *The Ornithology of Francis Willughby*, published in 1678, he wrote:

> What becomes of the Cuckow in the Winter-time, whether hiding her self in hollow Trees, or other holes and Caverns, she lies torpid, and at the return of the Spring revives again; or rather at the approach of Winter, being impatient of the cold, shifts place and departs into hot Countrys, is not as yet to me certainly known . . . Some . . . tell a story of a certain Country-man of Zurich in Switzerland, who having laid a log on the fire in Winter, heard a Cuckow cry in it . . . For my part I never yet met with any credible person that dared affirm that himself had found or seen a Cuckow in Winter-time taken out of a hollow tree, or any other lurking-place.

Even a century later, the migration versus hibernation debate still rumbled on in the letters of *The Natural History of Selborne*. However, by the early 1800s the evidence for migration had become overwhelming. Swallows and other migrants were observed leaving Britain in the autumn, flying south through Europe and then crossing the Mediterranean to Africa, with a return migration in the spring. During the next century it became clear that sub-Saharan Africa was the destination for many European migrants. Common cuckoos were recorded arriving in Senegal, West Africa, from late July through October, moving southeast along the African coast in December, and then returning northwest in February and March. Cuckoos also appeared in East and southern Africa, arriving from September to November, and then moving north again along the coast, and up the Rift Valley and Nile Valley in March and April.

Could the cuckoo decline be due to deteriorating conditions on migration, or in wintering sites south of the Sahara? The re-trapping of ringed birds in Britain had shown that 60 per cent of adult cuckoos survived to the next breeding season, but exactly where British cuckoos went to in Africa, and the route they took, was a mystery. Ninety years of ringing had produced just one recovery south of the Sahara: a cuckoo ringed as a chick in a pied wagtail nest in Eton on 23 June 1928 was killed in Cameroon, West Africa, on 30 January 1930.

Then, in May 2011 Chris Hewson, Phil Atkinson and their colleagues at the BTO caught five male cuckoos on their breeding grounds in Norfolk and fitted them with satellite tags. The tags are solar-powered and they transmit for 10 hours before going into 'sleep mode' for 48 hours while the solar panel recharges the battery. These tags are now giving spectacular results. Just as Edgar Chance's observations, 100 years ago, uncovered the difficulties that cuckoos face in laying their eggs in host nests, so Chris and Phil are now revealing that cuckoos have equally daunting problems on migration, as they struggle to survive through to the next breeding season.

The locations of the cuckoos were made available live on the internet, and thousands of people logged on to the BTO website to follow the incredible journeys as they unfolded. All five of the 'class of 2011' made it to their African winter quarters. Two flew southwest to Spain, where they spent a week or two fattening up for the next stage of their journey. Then they crossed the Mediterranean into Morocco, skirted the western edge of the Sahara to Senegal and the Gambia in West Africa, before heading east and reaching the Congo rainforests by the end of November.

The other three took a different route. They headed southeast to Italy, where they fattened up in the watershed of the river Po. They then crossed the Mediterranean and Sahara at their widest points, a 3,000-kilometre desert crossing through Algeria and Niger, and joined the other two cuckoos in the Congo by the end of November. For the first time in five months, all five cuckoos were once again together in the same country. The Congo rainforest was to be their main wintering area, and they remained here for three to five months. Feeding in the skies above the forests would be common swifts, also wintering here, to remind them of their summer days back in Britain.

Perhaps we, too, should pause for a moment. Many people in Britain think of the common cuckoo as a British bird that goes to Africa for the winter. However, satellite tracking now reveals that 'our' cuckoos are in Africa for 70 per cent of their lives. They spend twice as long with lowland gorillas in the wilds of the Congo forest as with cattle in the tamed countryside of Britain. Cuckoos might better be regarded as African birds that go to Britain for a short time each year to breed.

The return journey from the Congo to England was faster, taking just two months. First, the cuckoos flew to West Africa, where they spent a month or so, presumably preparing for their long migration north over the desert. Here they would meet wintering reed warblers, also getting ready for their journeys north. We might wonder if the two species pay any attention to one another, thousands of kilometres away from the reed beds of Europe, where they engage in such intense battles of host defence and cuckoo trickery.

After the desert crossing, the cuckoos recovered at stopover sites in southern Europe, but only two made it safely back to Norfolk. Signals from one ceased soon after it headed west from the Congo forest. Another cuckoo was lost in Spain during an unusually heavy hail storm. This bird had travelled south through Italy the previous autumn, showing that the return journey did not necessarily retrace the same migration route. A third cuckoo was lost soon after the northwards crossing of the Sahara.

The tracking reveals that cuckoos migrate almost exclusively by night, and often at high altitude, between three and five kilometres above the ground, perhaps where they are more likely to find strong following winds to help them on their way. However, the Sahara desert crossing is often made in one continuous flight of about 50–60 hours. We can imagine the cuckoos launching into the night skies at dusk. Then they will endure a remarkable non-stop flight: through night, day, night, day and then a third night on the wing, before they arrive the next dawn and have a chance to feed once more.

The routes of the two cuckoos that made it to Africa and back are shown here in the map, together with their journeys the following year. They took different routes, but ended up in the same wintering area in the Congo. Their detailed 'blogs', summarised here from the BTO's website by kind permission of Chris Hewson and Phil Atkinson, reveal all the drama of their migration.

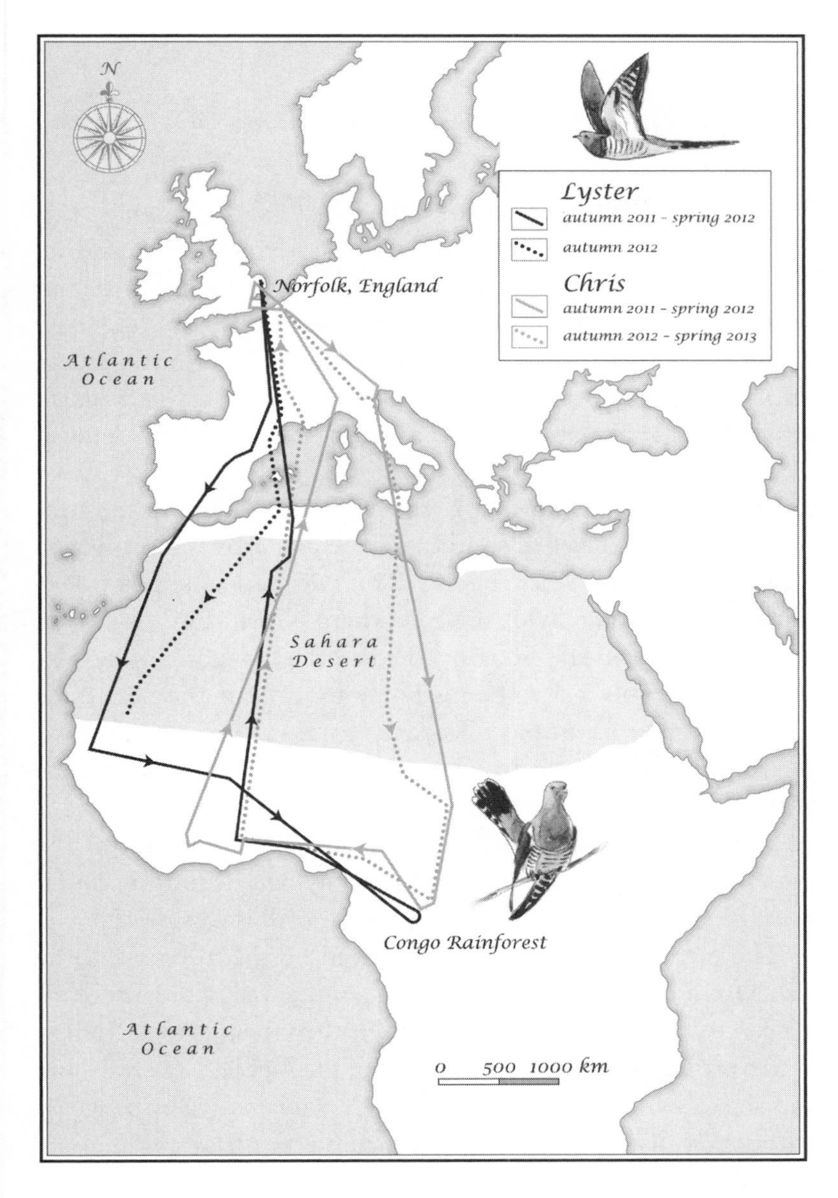

The migration routes of two male cuckoos caught in Norfolk, England, and fitted with satellite tags. Both spent the winter in the Congo forests, but Lyster took a southwesterly route through Spain, while Chris took a southeasterly route through Italy. From information kindly provided by Chris Hewson and Phil Atkinson, British Trust for Ornithology.

LYSTER'S BLOG: A SOUTHWESTERLY ROUTE

Lyster was caught on 25 May 2011 near Martham in the Norfolk Broads. He spent the summer in the Broads and then on 22 July he left, flying south through France and arriving east of Madrid, Spain on 27 July. He remained here for 11 days in an area of forest-clad mountains, presumably fattening up for the next stage. He departed on 8 August, crossed the Strait of Gibraltar, and arrived on the Atlantic coast of Morocco on 10 August, where he stayed in an area of ponds and bushes until 20 August.

The next signal, on 24 August, showed he had already crossed the Sahara and was now in northern Senegal. During the next two months he travelled southeast in stages, arriving in Burkina Faso on 4 October, where he stayed for two weeks in open woodland savannah, then flying on to southern Nigeria by 24 October. He finally crossed the Equator to reach the Congo rainforest by 29 October. This was to be his home for at least the next three and a half months, until 16 February 2012.

A signal on 6 March 2012 found him heading back westwards through Nigeria. He continued west, reaching Ghana on 7 March, where he remained for a month until 1 April, on the wooded shores of Lake Volta. Presumably he was putting on fat once more, to fuel his spring migration north across the Sahara.

The next signal, on 13 April, was from northern Algeria, so he had almost crossed the Sahara, taking a route well to the east of his desert crossing the previous autumn. He then spent 15 to 21 April in a date plantation in the northern part of the Algerian desert, before moving to some woodland in the Atlas Mountains, where he stayed for another three days. This long stop in North Africa was unusual, so perhaps he was exhausted by the desert crossing. Two other cuckoos disappeared at this stage, which suggests that the northward migration was particularly tough during spring 2012.

On 25 April Lyster left North Africa, and he then sped quickly northwards across the Mediterranean and up through France. He arrived just south of Paris on 27 April, and was back in the Norfolk Broads on 30 April, just 10 kilometres from where he had originally been caught the year before.

Lyster spent the summer in the Broads again, roaming widely, presumably in search of females. He was still there on 7 July 2012, but on 10 July had started his migration south and was crossing mid-France, reaching the border with Spain on 16 July. He spent 17 to 29 July near Barcelona in an area of flat, irrigated agricultural land. So although he was using the same overall southwest route once again, this was a different fattening-up site from the year before. On 1 August he had crossed the Mediterranean and was in northern Algeria. His last signal was on 8 August 2012, from the western edge of the Sahara in southern Mauritania. He had almost made it across the desert, but presumably he perished there in this barren and unforgiving landscape.

CHRIS'S BLOG: A SOUTHEASTERLY ROUTE

Chris was caught on 1 June 2011, near Santon Downham, in Thetford Forest, Norfolk, 70 kilometres west of Lyster. He was here until 4 June, but the next day he had flown south and was near Battle in East Sussex. He was still here on 15 June, but by 17 June he had flown east across the Channel and was in Belgium, where he remained in an area of woodland until 3 July. Had he started his migration a month earlier than Lyster? Or was he still in breeding mode and searching for females at new sites?

On 4 July, he had certainly started his journey and was heading south, reaching northern Italy on 6 July. He remained here until

20 July in the Po Delta World Heritage Site, an area of wetlands, presumably putting on fat ready for the desert crossing. On 23 July his signal showed he was in northern Chad, crossing the rugged mountains of the mid-Sahara. He had migrated 2,600 kilometres in just 56 hours. By 26 July, he had safely completed the desert crossing and was in southern Chad. The rains had just arrived in this area of savannah woodland, and Chris must have found a good feeding area because he remained here for 10 weeks until 2 October.

The next day he was on the move again, travelling south through the Central African Republic (4 to 9 October) and arriving in the rainforest of the northern Congo on 10 October. As for Lyster, this was to be his main wintering area, and he remained here for five months, until 2 March 2012. How truly remarkable it is that these two males, who both spent their summer in Norfolk, should reach the same wintering area in the Congo by such different routes.

On 3 March, Chris was travelling again, and had arrived in Cameroon. From 12 to 15 March he remained in southern Ghana, and then from 16 March to 2 April he was in the Ivory Coast. So both he and Lyster spent the third part of their winter in West Africa. His northward journey across the Sahara took a similar route to Lyster's, and was at about the same time, too, because by 7 April Chris was in northern Algeria. However, he then took a more easterly route across Europe, arriving in northern Italy on 11 April. He was apparently held here up by bad weather and didn't leave until 30 April. Then he made up for lost time and was in Essex, just north of London, on 1 May. By 4 May he was back in Thetford Forest, arriving on his old summer territory just three days later than Lyster had done.

Chris stayed in Thetford Forest for just five and a half weeks, again departing early, on 12 June. Then, just as in the previous year, he spent the second part of his summer in Belgium. So once again, having searched for female cuckoos in Norfolk, he may have turned his attention to females across the Channel. He must have started his migration south by 12 July, because on that day he was in northern Italy, in the watershed of the River Po. He was expected to stay here for a while to refuel, as he had done the previous year, but he surprised everyone by continuing south, and two days later he was in Sicily. By 17 July he had almost completed the Sahara crossing, and on 19 July he was just north of Lake Chad.

So his route across the Sahara was exactly the same southeasterly one as the year before, except for a little bow to the west in the southern Sahara, probably due to drift in a strong wind. He remained in Chad until early September, and then travelled south on exactly the same track as the previous year, reaching the Congo rainforest on 26 September. Here he stayed in the same general area as the winter before, until 6 March 2013.

His return movements were again similar to those of the previous spring: first across to West Africa, with a spell in Ghana (16 March to 1 April) in the Digya National Park, an area of forest and open woodland savannah, where he probably fattened up for migration, then the same route north across the Sahara, arriving in northern Algeria on 4 April, a remarkable 3,200-kilometre flight in about 60 hours. During April, Chris travelled north through France, but surprisingly he remained in the north of France until 3 May. Perhaps this time he was delayed by French female cuckoos? He finally arrived back in his old patch in Thetford Forest on 4 May, where he stayed until 21 June.

In late summer 2013, Chris was tracked on his southward migration for a third time (not shown on the map), again following the same southeasterly route. He repeated his previous habit of a trip to Belgium (21 June to 1 July), then flew to northern

Italy, where he remained for a while (3 to 21 July), before crossing the Sahara over the same route to southern Chad (22 to 25 July, a journey of 3,035 kilometres in three and a half days). He stayed here once more, for two months, before continuing south to arrive in his favourite main wintering area in the Congo on 26 September, exactly the same date as the year before.

Following their remarkable results from this first batch of tagged cuckoos, Chris and Phil have tagged more in subsequent years, including birds from Scotland, where there has been less of a decline in cuckoos than in England. It will be particularly interesting to see whether cuckoos from different parts of the UK have different migration routes and different wintering areas. Perhaps this may explain different population trends. So far, only males have been tagged, because the transmitters are too heavy for the lighter females. Improvements in technology will soon permit the tagging of females as well.

We still do not understand the causes of the cuckoo's precipitous decline, but perhaps the main message from this wonderful study is a broader one: we need international cooperation to ensure that cuckoos have suitable habitat at all stages of their lives, not just for breeding and wintering but also for their hazardous journeys during migration.

14

A changing world

A meadow pipit feeding a fledged young cuckoo.
Dartmoor, 29 July 2007.

Sumer is icumen in,
Lhude sing cuccu!

Are we about to lose our harbinger of spring?

The dramatic decline in cuckoos across England during the last three decades is reflected by the changes we have recorded on Wicken Fen. In 1985, the first year of our study, there were 14 female cuckoos parasitising reed warblers on the Fen, recognisable by their individually distinctive eggs. In the last four years, to 2013, there have been just one or two females. In 2012, not a single cuckoo chick was raised to independence on the Fen, the first time this has happened during the 30 years of our study, and perhaps the first time for hundreds of years.

Our records show that reed warbler numbers on the Fen have not changed, so the decline in cuckoos has led to a marked reduction in parasitism, from 24 per cent of reed warbler nests in 1985 to just 1 per cent in 2012.

Humans are not the only ones to have noticed that cuckoos are becoming scarcer. Remarkably, the reed warblers have noticed it too. Our experiments show that reed warblers are now much more reluctant to approach and mob an adult cuckoo than they were back in the 1980s, and they are also less likely to reject a cuckoo egg. This is not simply a general reduction in their response to any threat, because reed warblers have shown no changes during the last three decades in their responses to other enemies, such as sparrowhawks (a predator of adult reed warblers) or jays (a nest predator).

Why have reed warbler defences against cuckoos declined, now that there is little threat of parasitism? Their change in behaviour makes good economic sense. We have seen in previous chapters that defences are costly. Cuckoos resemble hawks, so it is dangerous to approach a cuckoo-like enemy at the nest. A mistake could be fatal. Cuckoo eggs resemble host eggs, so egg ejection is costly too: sometimes hosts reject their own eggs in error. If reed warblers assess that there are few or no cuckoos, then their best option is to avoid these risks of making mistakes. We invest less in costly defences of our property when the risk of burglary is low. Reed warblers, too, invest less in their cuckoo defences when the risk of parasitism declines.

How have reed warblers adapted so rapidly? Sometimes populations adapt to a changing world by genetic changes. Darwin assumed that such evolution by natural selection would proceed so slowly that we would never be able to observe the changes in progress. Indeed, *The Origin of Species* does not document any cases of natural selection in action, only the outcomes of past selection, and in a famous passage Darwin wrote:

> natural selection is daily and hourly scrutinising, throughout the world, the slightest variations; rejecting those that are bad, preserving and adding up all that are good . . . [but] we see nothing of these slow changes in progress, until the hand of time has marked the lapse of ages.

However, we now know of many examples where genetic variants have such a strong selective advantage in nature that we can watch evolutionary change taking place even within a few years.

Peter Berthold and colleagues from the Max Planck Institute at Radolfzell, Germany, have discovered a wonderful example of evolutionary change in migration due to climate change. During the past 40 years the number of blackcaps wintering in Britain and Ireland has steadily increased. At first, it was assumed that these must be British and Irish breeders, remaining in response to milder winters. However, ringing recoveries indicate that they are breeders from central Europe with an entirely new migration habit of going northwest in the autumn instead of following the traditional route, southwest to the Mediterranean. Berthold was able to study the migration direction of blackcaps in the laboratory by keeping them in small cages. During the migration period, the birds flutter against one side of the cage, indicating the direction they want to fly. When blackcaps wintering in Britain were tested, they exhibited a northwest preference in autumn, a 70-degree shift in direction from the traditional southwesterly route. Furthermore, when these birds that wintered in Britain were bred in aviaries, it was found that their offspring inherited this new autumnal orientation.

In past times, when winters were more severe, mutant blackcaps with this new migration direction would have been eliminated by natural selection. But now the new migration habit is flourishing because of milder weather and more winter food in Britain, both from garden feeders and from winter-fruiting bushes planted in recent decades. This new population of migrants not only enjoys a shorter distance to winter quarters, but also an earlier arrival back in the central European breeding grounds in spring. Stuart Bearhop and colleagues, from the University of Exeter, have shown that this enables them to gain the best breeding territories and to produce more offspring. They also discovered that the difference in arrival times on the breeding grounds results in matings between individuals from the same wintering area. For example, males wintering in Britain arrive early on the breeding territories and tend to pair with early-arriving females, which have also wintered in Britain. The consequence is reduced gene exchange between individuals with different migration habits, which has speeded up the evolution of the new migration behaviour.

Is the rapid decline in reed warbler defences against cuckoos on Wicken Fen also a case of evolutionary change by natural selection? My colleagues and I doubt this, not only because our calculations show that the decline has been too fast to reflect a genetic change in behaviour, but also because we know from experiments that individuals have remarkable flexibility in their levels of defence. When we presented mounts of adult cuckoos at nests, reed warblers were more likely to reject eggs. Their mobbing calls also attracted neighbours, which then increased their defences back at their own nests. The magnitudes of these individual changes in defences are similar to the declines we have seen over the last three decades. Therefore it is likely that the changes we have recorded in the population are entirely a reflection of flexible behaviour: reed warblers monitor local cuckoo activity, and they have reduced their defences because they perceive parasitism risk to be lower.

Why should reed warblers have such flexible cuckoo defences? Across most of Europe and throughout the UK, their populations are often restricted to small islands of wetland in a vast sea of agriculture. Cuckoo numbers are therefore often also small on a local scale, so parasitism is prone to chance variation between neighbouring sites and between years. Furthermore, although ringing recoveries show that some young reed warblers return to breed at their natal site, some disperse to breed up to 200 kilometres away (their average dispersal distance is 50 kilometres), and so they are likely to encounter different parasitism rates from those experienced by their parents. Whenever there is such fine-scale spatial and temporal variation in encounter rate with enemies, it makes good sense for individuals to vary their defences in response to local risks.

For example, in the mid-1980s, cuckoo parasitism on Wicken Fen was high (16 to 24 per cent annually), and our experiments there showed that reed warblers rejected 74 per cent of our model cuckoo eggs that differed in appearance from their own eggs. However, in a small reed bed just 11 kilometres away, where there were no cuckoos, the reed warblers accepted all our model cuckoo eggs. A wider analysis, comparing different populations across Europe, also shows that reed warblers vary their strength of egg rejection in response to parasitism risk. Once reed warblers are equipped to respond to this local variation in parasitism, they are bound to show rapid declines in defences as cuckoos decline.

There are other examples where birds have adapted to a rapidly changing world by individual flexibility in behaviour, rather than by genetic change in the population. In Wytham Woods, near Oxford, female great tits have advanced their egg laying by 14 days over the 47-year period 1961 to 2007. The main changes have been from the mid-1970s, since when there has been a marked increase in spring temperatures. This has led to the earlier emergence of oak leaves and of winter moth caterpillars, which feed on the oak leaves and are a key food for nestling great tits. The earlier laying of the great tits has tracked these earlier springs perfectly, so they still have chicks in the nest at the right time to coincide with the caterpillar peak. Anne Charmantier, Ben Sheldon and their colleagues from the University of Oxford have shown that this change in egg-laying date is entirely due to flexibility in the timing of laying by individual female great tits, perhaps a direct response to spring temperature or leaf burst or some other cue of the timing of the food peak.

Reed warblers and great tits have tracked their changing world by individually flexible defences and breeding times. However, their ability to respond so effectively depends on reliable cues of change, such as observing fewer cuckoos or detecting earlier springs. When cues are not available, it will be impossible for an individual to track change by varying its behaviour. For example, many long-distance migrants, which spend the winter in Africa south of the Sahara, now arrive too late to catch the earlier spring food peak in their northern European breeding grounds. This is because their spring departure from African winter quarters is triggered by changes in day length, unaffected by climate change. Natural selection will now be favouring individuals whose response to day length leads to earlier departures, but it will take time for a population to evolve a new habit. It is still unclear to what extent genetic change will enable animals to keep pace with our rapidly changing world.

Animals and plants have evolved in response to environmental change ever since life began, for example with changes on the grand scale of shifting continents and ice ages. For thousands of years they have been faced with human-induced changes, too, as our ancestors cut down forests, burnt grasslands, and flooded or drained the land. But the current scale and pace of change is unprecedented, involving climate change, habitat destruction and fragmentation, ever more intensive farming and fishing, urbanisation, and a new biotic environment of invasive species, pathogens and parasites. When I was a young boy, I thought there would always be cuckoos calling to greet the spring, and swifts would forever scythe the skies on hot summer days. But the alarming declines in populations of these and many other familiar species mean that our generation will surely be the last to take the natural world for granted. The title of a recent seminar by my colleague at Cambridge, Andrew Balmford, Professor of Conservation Science, neatly captures our dilemma: 'How to feed the world without costing the earth'.

One of the ways we must help is by preserving and creating more suitable habitat for wildlife. For example, there are now plans to extend the areas of wetland in the old fens of eastern England, partly to compensate for the imminent loss of coastal wetlands, which are threatened by rising sea levels. The new reserve of the Royal Society for the Protection of Birds (RSPB) at Lakenheath is an inspiring example of what can be achieved in a short time. From 1996 to 2004, a 200-hectare area of wetland was created to the south of the Little Ouse River, on the Norfolk–Suffolk border, from land that had been drained at various times from the seventeenth to the nineteenth centuries and converted to arable land in the 1950s. The development of the reserve, led by Norman Sills, the first site manager, and Graham Hirons, chief ecologist at the RSPB, involved transforming carrot fields to a mosaic of washland, pools and wet grassland, with new reed beds created by the planting by hand of over 300,000 reed seedlings and stems. At the time the reserve was set up, the purchase cost of the land plus the capital cost of converting it to a wetland reserve was 1.5 million pounds, about the same as the cost of a large four-bedroomed detached house in a smart part of Cambridge.

By 2010, this new reserve already had thriving populations of Britain's most characteristic wetland birds, including 12 marsh harrier nests, which produced 30 fledged young that year, four bittern nests, over 100 pairs of bearded tits, several hundred pairs of reed warblers, and, most exciting of all, the first cranes to breed in the fens for 400 years. William Turner mentions cranes in his 1544 book: 'Cranes . . . breed in England in marshy places. I myself have very often seen their pipers [young].' However, it is likely that they became extinct as a breeding bird in Britain during the sixteenth century, 100 years before the extensive draining of the Fens. The menu for King Henry III's banquet in 1251 points to the likely cause of their demise: it included 115 cranes, along with 430 red deer, 1,300 hares, 2,100 partridges, 395 swans, 120 peafowl and lampreys 'without number'.

With their elegant stature, strength and grace in flight and melancholic bugling cries, cranes have a rich mythology as symbols of vigilance, wisdom, longevity and good fortune. They are often regarded as birds from heaven, whose powerful wings can transport humans to greater spiritual enlightenment. They are the perfect symbol of wilderness, an 'umbrella species' whose protection will ensure the survival of wider biodiversity. Cranes are now spreading to other fenland reserves, which are being restored and extended around the washlands of the Great Ouse and Nene rivers. There are also plans to create a large wetland linking the two National Nature Reserves, Woodwalton Fen and Holme Fen, and to extend Wicken Fen, too, perhaps as far south as Cambridge.

As I write these last paragraphs, it is early April and I'm back on Wicken Fen once more, preparing for another season. Cuckoos and reed warblers will have left their winter quarters south of the Sahara, and will be on their way north. I am excited at the prospect of their arrival – hearing their songs once again, finding the first reed warbler nest of the summer and the first clutch with a cuckoo egg.

Marsh harriers are already building nests in the reed beds, and I lie on my back to marvel at the males' wonderfully exuberant skydiving displays, high over the fen. As thermals develop in the warmth of the early-morning sunshine, they begin to soar, silently, on upswept wings, and to such great heights that they become difficult to pick out with the naked eye against the blue of the sky or billowing white clouds. Then, when they reach the summit of their ascent, they begin an undulating flight, with slow flaps, interspersed with spectacular dives and somersaults, the silver undersides of their wings flashing like mirrors in the sun, and calling all the while with a shrill two-note '*way-ee, way-ee*'. The display may last for 10 or 20 minutes as the male plunges down with closed or partly closed wings, spinning and twisting as he descends, sometimes looping the loop as he flips through a complete revolution before sweeping up again to maintain his elevation.

As I watch, I think of the vast wilderness their ancestors would have surveyed in William Turner's time, and I wonder if their descendants will soar again one day over a wetland that stretches the 15 kilometres to my home city of Cambridge. Meanwhile, in a week or so, my reed warblers will drop from the night skies to this little patch of fen. My hopes are that some cuckoos will follow them, to thrill naturalists once more with their curious breeding habits, and as harbingers of a new spring.

Notes to the chapters

PREFACE

For more on cuckoos and human culture, see Mark Cocker and Richard Mabey, *Birds Britannica* (Chatto & Windus, 2005); Mark Cocker and David Tipling, *Birds and People* (Jonathan Cape, 2013); and Michael McCarthy, *Say Goodbye to the Cuckoo* (John Murray, 2009). The early reference to cuckoos by Hesiod is in M. L. West, *Hesiod: Works & Days* (Oxford University Press, 1978). The letters to *The Times* are in Kenneth Gregory, *The First Cuckoo: Letters to The Times Since 1900* (Allen & Unwin, 1976). The account of the February cuckoo that was shot is from Michael Walters, *A Concise History of Ornithology* (Helm, 2003).

The poem by Jane Taylor is one in a set of songs, *Friday Afternoons*, by Benjamin Britten. The lines by Ted Hughes are from his poem 'Cuckoo'; see his *Collected Poems*, edited by Paul Keegan (Faber and Faber, 2003).

Turner's book on birds is W. Turner, *A Short and Succinct History of the Principal Birds Noticed by Pliny and Aristotle* (1544), edited by A. H. Evans (Cambridge University Press, 1903).

For a wonderful account of the joys and inspiration of bird watching, see Jeremy Mynott, *Birdscapes: Birds in Our Imagination and Experience* (Princeton University Press, 2009).

CHAPTER 1. A CUCKOO IN THE NEST

For Aristotle's account of the cuckoo laying eggs in other birds' nests, see A. L. Peck, *Aristotle: Historia Animalium*, Volume 2 (Heinemann, 1970); and for his account of the young cuckoo ejecting host eggs, see W. S. Hett, *Aristotle: Minor Works. On Marvellous Things Heard* (Heinemann, 1936). The 1248 quote from Frederick II of Hohenstaufen is from C. A. Wood & F. M. Fyfe, *The Art of Falconry, Being the De arte venandi cum avibus of Frederick the Second of Hohenstaufen* (Stanford University Press, 1943).

Sir John Clanvowe's (1341–1391) poem is in *The Boke of Cupide, God of Love, or The Cuckoo and the Nightingale*, edited by Dana M. Symons (Western Michigan University, 2004), available online: http://www.lib.rochester.edu/camelot/teams/sym1frm.htm

The John Ray quote is from his book *The Ornithology of Francis Willughby* (John Martyn, London, 1678). I am indebted to Tim Birkhead for this reference; see Tim's wonderful book *The Wisdom of Birds* (Bloomsbury, 2008), for the influence of Ray on ornithology.

Hérissant's paper on cuckoo guts is in *Histoire de L'Académie Royale* (1752), 417–423. Gilbert White discusses cuckoos in several letters in *The Natural History of Selborne* (1789), edited by R. Mabey (Penguin, 1977). Edward Jenner's classic paper is in *Philosophical Transactions of the Royal Society of London* (1788), 78, 219–237. The Bechstein quote on benevolent hosts is in J. M. Bechstein, *Gemeinnützige Naturgeschichte Deutschlands*, Bd 2 (Crusius, Leipzig, 1791). For other references to early accounts of cuckoos, see K. Schulze-Hagen *et al.*, *Journal of Ornithology* (2009), 150, 1–16; and N. B. Davies, *Cuckoos, Cowbirds and Other Cheats* (T. & A. D. Poyser, 2000). This last book reviews all the brood-parasitic birds.

Charles Willson Peale's comments on the admirable family life of American cuckoo species with parental care are from Richard Conniff, *The Species Seekers: Heroes, Fools and the Mad Pursuit of Life on Earth* (Norton, New York, 2011).

The family tree of cuckoos analysed by molecular genetics, by Michael Sorenson and Robert Payne, is in R. B. Payne, *The Cuckoos* (Oxford University Press, 2005). The classic paper on evolutionary arms races, by Richard Dawkins and John Krebs, is in *Proceedings of the Royal Society B* (1979), 205, 489–511.

CHAPTER 2. HOW THE CUCKOO LAYS HER EGG

Edgar Chance published two books on cuckoos: *The Cuckoo's Secret* (Sidgwick & Jackson, 1922); *The Truth about the Cuckoo* (Country Life, 1940).

Baldamus and Rey's studies in Germany are: E. Baldamus, *Das Leben der Europäischen Kuckucke* (Parey, 1892); E. Rey, *Altes und Neues aus dem Haushalte des Kuckucks* (Freese, 1892). Alfred Newton's article on cuckoo races is in *A Dictionary of Birds* (A. & C. Black, 1893). Karsten Gärtner's studies are in *Ornithologische Mitteilungen* (1981), 33, 115–131, and *Die Vogelwelt* (1982), 103, 201–224.

For genetic differences between the races of common cuckoos, see F. Fossøy *et al. Proceedings of the Royal Society B* (2011), 278, 1639–1645.

Mike Bayliss celebrates the egg-laying record by his cuckoo in *BTO News* (1988), 159, 7.

CHAPTER 3. WICKEN FEN

The history of Wicken Fen and more about the reserve and its wildlife is in the book edited by Laurie Friday, *Wicken Fen: the Making of a Wetland Nature Reserve* (Harley Books, 1997). For the history of the fens, see Oliver Rackham's book *The History of the Countryside* (Dent, 1986), and Ian D. Rotherham's *The Lost Fens: England's Greatest Ecological Disaster* (The History Press, 2013). The Guthlac poem translation is from S. A. J. Bradley, *Anglo-Saxon Poetry* (Everyman, 2004).

Eric Ennion's accounts of bird watching and drawing in the fens are in his books: *Adventurers Fen* (Methuen, 1942); *Birds and Seasons* (Arlequin Press, 1994): and *One Man's Birds* (The Wildlife Art Gallery, Lavenham, 2004). For a lyrical account of the old fens and Ennion's fen as it is today, see the wonderful book by Tim Dee, *Four Fields* (Jonathan Cape, 2013).

CHAPTER 4. HARBINGER OF SPRING

For more on reed warblers, see Bernd Leisler and Karl Schulze-Hagen, *The Reed Warblers: Diversity in a Uniform Bird Family* (KNNV Publishing, 2011). For details of reed warbler breeding behaviour on Wicken Fen, see N. B. Davies *et al.*, *Animal Behaviour* (2003), 65, 285–295. For discussion of fidelity and extra-pair matings in birds, see Tim Birkhead's book *Promiscuity: an Evolutionary History of Sperm Competition and Sexual Conflict* (Faber & Faber, 2000).

For radio-tracking studies of cuckoos, see I. Wyllie, *The Cuckoo* (Batsford, 1981); H. Nakamura & Y. Miyazawa, *Japanese Journal of Ornithology* (1997), 46, 23–54; M. Honza *et al.*, *Animal Behaviour* (2002), 64, 861–868. For greater parasitism rates of host nests near cuckoo vantage posts, see F. Alvarez, *Ibis* (1993), 135, 331; I. J. Øien *et al.*, *Journal of Animal Ecology* (1996), 65, 147–153; and J. A. Welbergen & N. B. Davies, *Current Biology* (2009), 19, 235–240. For studies of cuckoo paternity and mating systems, see D. A. Jones *et al.*, *Ibis* (1997), 139, 560–562, and K. Marchetti *et al.*, *Science* (1998), 282, 471–472. For evidence, from

DNA profiles, that individual female cuckoos lay a constant egg type, see A. Moksnes *et al.*, *Journal of Avian Biology* (2008), 39, 238–241.

CHAPTER 5. PLAYING CUCKOO

Experimental studies of how cuckoo hosts respond to foreign eggs were pioneered by E. C. S. Baker, *Ibis* (1913), 55, 384–398, and *Proceedings of the Zoological Society of London* (1923), 277–294; and by C. F. M. Swynnerton, *Ibis* (1918), 60, 127–154. My experimental study of reed warblers and cuckoos on Wicken Fen with Mike Brooke is N. B. Davies & M. de L. Brooke, *Animal Behaviour* (1988), 36, 262–284. See also the recent commentary by M. C. Stoddard & R. M. Kilner, *Animal Behaviour* (2013), 85, 693–699.

Wallace's discussion of camouflage is in his book *Darwinism: an Exposition of the Theory of Natural Selection with Some of its Applications* (Macmillan, 1889).

For a detailed study of how cuckoos lay in reed warbler nests, see A. Moksnes *et al.*, *Ibis* (2000), 142, 247–258. Anton Antonov *et al.*, *Chinese Birds* (2012), 3, 245–258, consider why cuckoos and other brood-parasitic birds have strong-shelled eggs.

CHAPTER 6. AN ARMS RACE WITH EGGS

For studies of how various hosts respond to model cuckoo eggs, see N. B. Davies & M. de L. Brooke, *Journal of Animal Ecology* (1989), 58, 207–224 and 225–236; A. Moksnes *et al.*, *Auk* (1991), 108, 348–354, and *Behaviour* (1991), 116, 64–89. John Owen's study of cuckoos parasitising dunnocks is in *Report of the Felsted School Science Society* (1933), 33, 25–39. For evidence that the cuckoo race specialising on dunnocks lays a distinct egg type, see

M. de L. Brooke & N. B. Davies, *Nature* (1988), 335, 630–632. And for genetic differences among cuckoo races in Britain, see H. L. Gibbs *et al. Nature* (2000), 407, 183–186.

For cuckoo egg mimicry, as seen through a bird's eye, see M. C. Stoddard & M. Stevens, *Proceedings of the Royal Society B* (2010), 277, 1387–1393, and *Evolution* (2011), 65, 2004–2013. For evolution of thicker cuckoo eggshells in response to host rejection, see C. N. Spottiswoode, *Journal of Evolutionary Biology* (2010), 23, 1792–1799.

The arms race between water fleas and their bacteria parasites is in E. Decaestecker *et al.*, *Nature* (2007), 450, 870–873.

For cuckoo parasitism rates of British hosts, see M. de L. Brooke & N. B. Davies, *Journal of Animal Ecology* (1987), 56, 873–883. For more on the dunnock as a possible recent host, and the time to evolve egg rejection, see N. B. Davies & M. de L. Brooke, *Journal of Animal Ecology* (1989), 58, 225–236

CHAPTER 7. SIGNATURES AND FORGERIES

For reminiscences of Charles Swynnerton, see G. A. K. Marshall, *Nature* (1938), 142, 198–199; M. J. Kimberley, *Heritage* (1990), 9, 47–61. Swynnerton's classic paper on egg signatures is *Ibis* (1918), 60, 127–154. R. M. Kilner, *Biological Reviews* (2006), 81, 383–406, is a review of egg colours and patterns in birds. B. Igic *et al.*, *Proceedings of the Royal Society B* (2012), 279, 1068–1076, show that cuckoo-host egg mimicry involves use of the same eggshell pigments.

For evidence that egg patterns evolve as signatures in response to brood parasitism, see B. G. Stokke *et al.*, *Evolution* (2002), 56, 199–205; J. J. Soler & A. P. Møller, *Behavioural Ecology* (1996), 7, 89–94. The studies by Claire Spottiswoode and Martin Stevens of egg signatures in prinias in Africa, and their forgeries by cuckoo finches, are discussed in three papers: C. N. Spottiswoode & M. Stevens, *Proceedings of the National Academy of Sciences of the USA* (2010), 107, 8672–8676; *Proceedings of the Royal Society B* (2011), 278, 3566–3573; *American Naturalist* (2012), 179, 633–648. For an obituary of Major John Colebrook-Robjent, by Pete Leonard, see the *Bulletin of the African Bird Club* (2008), 16, 5; and for an evocative account of him and his remarkable collaboration with Claire Spottiswoode, see Tim Dee's book *The Running Sky* (Jonathan Cape, 2009). Extracts from the Major's diary are quoted by kind permission of Claire Spottiswoode and Ian Bruce-Miller.

For more on the introduction of village weaverbirds from Africa to the cuckoo-free islands of Hispaniola in the West Indies and Mauritius in the Indian Ocean, see David Lahti's paper in *Animal Biodiversity and Conservation* (2003), 26, 45–55. I am indebted to David for the reference and translation from Médéric Louis Élie Moreau de Saint-Méry, *Description topographique, physique, civile, politique et historique de la partie française de l'isle Saint-Domingue* (Chez Dupont, Paris, 1797), p. 426. For reference to the presence of a colony of weaverbirds in Tron Caiman, Haiti, in 1783, see W. D. Fitzwater, The weaver finch of Hispaniola, *Pest Control* (1971), 39, 19–20, 56–59. David Lahti's papers on the loss of egg signatures in village weaverbirds, when they were released from cuckoo parasitism, are: *Proceedings of the National Academy of Sciences of the USA* (2005), 102, 18057–18062; *Evolution* (2006), 60, 157–168. His paper on the influence of solar radiation on egg colour is: D. Lahti, *The Auk* (2008), 125, 796–802.

For evidence that hosts learn what their own eggs look like, see A. Lotem *et al.*, *Animal Behaviour* (1995), 49, 1185–1209; S. I. Rothstein, *Animal Behaviour* (1975), 23, 268–278. For how reed warblers vary their egg rejection thresholds according to perceived risks of parasitism, see N. B. Davies *et al.*, *Proceedings of the Royal Society B* (1996) 263, 925–931.

CHAPTER 8. A CHEAT IN VARIOUS GUISES

The classic paper on mimicry by Henry Walter Bates is *Transactions of the Linnean Society of London* (1862), 23, 495–566. For a biography of Wallace, see Peter Raby, *Alfred Russel Wallace: a Life* (Random House, 2002). Wallace's ideas on cuckoo hawk mimicry are in *Darwinism: an Exposition of the Theory of Natural Selection with Some of its Applications.*(Macmillan, 1889). Wallace suggested that cuckoos gained an advantage by mimicking hawks because it protected them from hawk attacks. For evidence that cuckoos suffer less from hawk predation than expected, see A. P. Møller *et al.*, *Journal of Avian Biology* (2012), 43, 390–396.

The description of the sparrowhawk's 'lunacy' is in W. K. Richmond, *British Birds of Prey* (Lutterworth, 1959), and quoted from Mark Cocker & Richard Mabey, *Birds Britannica* (Chatto & Windus, 2005). The Ted Hughes poem is 'Hawk roosting': see Ted Hughes, *Collected Poems*, edited by Paul Keegan (Faber & Faber, 2003).

For more on cuckoo hawk resemblance, see T.-L. Gluckman & N. I. Mundy, *Animal Behaviour* (2013), 86, 1165–1181. For evidence that hawk-like plumage, with underpart barring, is more prevalent in parasitic cuckoos, see O. Krüger *et al.*, *Proceedings of the Royal Society B* (2007), 274, 1553–1560. For experiments showing that hawk mimicry by cuckoos aids approach of reed warbler nests, see J. A. Welbergen & N. B. Davies, *Behavioural Ecology* (2011) 22, 574–579. For evidence that host mobbing of cuckoos deters parasitism, see J. A. Welbergen & N. B. Davies, *Current Biology* (2009), 19, 235–240;

and the review by W. E. Feeney *et al.*, *Animal Behaviour* (2012), 84, 3–12.

Experiments showing social transmission of mobbing responses by reed warblers are in N. B. Davies & J. A. Welbergen, *Science* (2009), 324, 1318–1320; D. Campobello & S. G. Sealy, *Behavioural Ecology* (2011), 22, 422–428; R. Thorogood & N. B. Davies, *Science* (2012), 337, 578–580.

CHAPTER 9. A STRANGE AND ODIOUS INSTINCT

Aristotle's mention of cuckoo chick ejection behaviour is in W. S. Hett, *Aristotle: Minor Works. On Marvellous Things Heard* (Heinemann, 1936). Jenner's wonderful description is in *Philosophical Transactions of the Royal Society of London* (1788), 78, 219–237. For other early accounts, see J. Blackwall, *Memoires of the Literary and Philosophical Society of Manchester, second series* (1824), 78, 441–472; G. Montagu, *Ornithological Dictionary of British Birds*, second edition (London, 1831); E. Baldamus, *Das Leben der Europäischen Kuckucke* (Parey, 1892).

Eviction behaviour of cuckoo chicks in reed and great reed warbler nests in the Czech Republic is described in M. Honza *et al.*, *Journal of Avian Biology* (2007), 38, 385–389; and in reed warbler nests in the English fens in I. Wyllie, *The Cuckoo* (Batsford, 1981).

Internal incubation of cuckoo eggs was first suggested by G. Montagu, *Ornithological Dictionary* (London, 1802), and first clearly demonstrated by T. R. Birkhead *et al.*, *Proceedings of the Royal Society B* (2011) 278, 1019–1024.

For sibling rivalry in birds and other animals, see D. W. Mock & G. A. Parker, *The Evolution of Sibling Rivalry* (Oxford, 1997). Honeyguide stabbing of host chicks is in C. N. Spottiswoode & J. Koorevaar, *Biology Letters* (2012), 8, 241–244. For stabbing with bill hooks during sibling rivalry in two parental species of birds, a bee-eater and a kookaburra, see D. M. Bryant & P. Tatner, *Animal Behaviour* (1990), 39, 657–671, and S. Legge, *Journal of Avian Biology* (2002), 33, 159–166.

The lack of chick rejection by reed warblers is shown by experiments in N. B. Davies & M. de L. Brooke, *Animal Behaviour* (1988), 36, 262–284. The suggestion that cuckoo chicks have a 'drug-like' manipulative effect on hosts is in R. Dawkins & J. R. Krebs, *Proceedings of the Royal Society B* (1979), 205, 489–511. Arnon Lotem's paper on why, in theory, hosts might be doomed to accept common cuckoo chicks is in *Nature* (1993), 362, 743–745.

For the Australian aboriginal legend explaining why cuckoos do not raise their own young, see http://newsok. com/the-cuckoos-rebellion/article/2626984. For aboriginal knowledge that fairy-wrens do not reject bronze-cuckoo eggs, see S. C. Tidemann & T. Whiteside, Aboriginal stories: the riches and colour of Australian birds, in *Ethno-Ornithology: Birds and Indigenous People, Culture and Society* (London, Earthscan, 2011), pp. 153–179. For rejection of bronze-cuckoo chicks by hosts in Australia, see N. E. Langmore *et al.*, *Nature* (2003), 422, 157–160, and *Behavioural Ecology* (2009), 20, 978–984; N. J. Sato *et al.*, *Biology Letters* (2010), 6, 67–69; and K. Tokue & K. Ueda, *Ibis* (2010), 152, 835–839. For mimicry of host chicks by bronze-cuckoo chicks, see N. E. Langmore, *Proceedings of the Royal Society B* (2011), 278, 2455–2463.

For estimates of the age of cuckoo host-races in Britain, see H. L. Gibbs *et al.*, *Nature* (2000), 407, 183–186. For dark, cryptic cuckoo eggs in some bronze-cuckoos, see N. E. Langmore *et al.* *Animal Behaviour* (2009), 78, 461–468.

CHAPTER 10. BEGGING TRICKS

For desertion of cuckoos in response to a prolonged period of care, see T. Grim *et al.*, *Proceedings of the Royal Society B* (2003), 270, Supplement, S73–S75; and T. Grim, *Proceedings of the Royal Society B* (2007), 274, 373–381.

The stimulating effect of the cuckoo chick's gape for rufous bush chat hosts is shown in F. Alvarez, *Ardea* (2004), 92, 63–68. The effect of the cuckoo chick's rapid begging calls on host provisioning is shown in N. B. Davies *et al.*, *Proceedings of the Royal Society B* (1998), 265, 673–678; and R. M. Kilner *et al.*, *Nature* (1999), 397, 667–672. J. H. Zorn had already suggested this idea back in 1743 in his book *Petinotheologie* (Enderes, Schwabach). The rapid begging calls of honeyguide chicks were noted by C. H. Fry, *Bulletin of the British Ornithologists' Club* (1974), 94, 58–59. The false gapes on the underwings of Horsfield's hawk-cuckoos are in K. D. Tanaka & K. Ueda, *Science* (2005), 308, 653; and K. D. Tanaka *et al.*, *Journal of Avian Biology* (2005), 36, 461–464.

The effectiveness of eye images at manipulating human behaviour is shown in M. Bateson *et al.*, *Biology Letters* (2006), 2, 412–414, and *PLoS One* (2012), 7, e51738.

For how cuckoo chicks respond to host alarm calls, see N. B. Davies *et al.*, *Proceedings of the Royal Society B* (2006), 273, 693–699. For begging stimuli that great spotted cuckoo chicks use to outcompete host chicks, see M. Soler *et al.*, *Behavioural Ecology and Sociobiology* (1995), 37, 7–13; T. Redondo, *Etologia* (1993), 3, 235–297. For why magpie host parents might naturally prefer large, hungry chicks, see M. Husby, *Journal of Animal Ecology* (1986), 55, 75–83.

CHAPTER 11. CHOOSING HOSTS

Gilbert White's (1789) *The Natural History of Selborne* is edited by R. Mabey (Penguin, 1977). Edward Jenner's paper is in *Philosophical Transactions of the Royal Society of London* (1788), 78, 219–237. The unsuitability of blackbirds and song thrushes as cuckoo hosts is shown experimentally by T. Grim *et al.*, *Journal of Animal Ecology* (2011), 80, 508–518. The idea that some species are old hosts, which won the arms race with cuckoos, is discussed in N. B. Davies & M. de L. Brooke, *Journal of Animal Ecology* (1989), 58, 207–224 and 225–236; A. Moksnes *et al.*, *Behaviour* (1991), 116, 64–89; S. I. Rothstein, *Animal Behaviour* (2001), 61, 95–107; R. M. Kilner & N. E. Langmore, *Biological Reviews* (2011), 86, 836–852.

Habitat imprinting by cuckoos is shown in Y. Teuschl *et al.*, *Animal Behaviour* (1998), 56, 1425–1433. Host imprinting in indigobirds is shown in R. B. Payne *et al.*, *Animal Behaviour* (2000), 59, 69–81.

For natal dispersal of nestling cuckoos, see D. C. Seel, *Ibis* (1977), 119, 309-322. For host fidelity by female cuckoos, see M. Honza *et al.*, *Animal Behaviour* (2002), 64, 861–868; S. Skjelseth *et al.*, *Journal of Avian Biology* (2004), 35, 21–24; K. Marchetti *et al.*, *Science* (1998), 282, 471–472. R. C. Punnett's article suggesting that a female's egg colour in cuckoos might be determined by her mother's genes is in *Nature* (1933), 132, 892. For genetic differences between the cuckoo races, see F. Fossøy *et al.*, *Proceedings of the Royal Society B* (2011), 278, 1639–1645; O. Krüger & M. Kolss, *Journal of Evolutionary Biology* (2013), 26, 2447–2457. For call differences among male cuckoos in areas with different host species, see T. I. Fuisz & S. R. de Kort, *Proceedings of the Royal Society B* (2007), 274, 2093–2097.

H. N. Southern's article is in *Evolution as a Process*, edited by J. S. Huxley, A. C. Hardy & E. B. Ford (Allen & Unwin,

1954), pp. 219–232. For frequency of mismatching eggs in host clutches in museum collections, see A. Moksnes & E. Røskaft, *Journal of Zoology, London* (1995), 236, 625–648. For the start of a new race of cuckoo in Japan, see H. Nakamura, *Japanese Journal of Ornithology* (1990), 46, 23–54; H. Nakamura *et al.*, in *Parasitic Birds and their Hosts*, edited by S. I. Rothstein & S. K. Robinson (Oxford University Press, 1998), pp. 94–112.

CHAPTER 12. AN ENTANGLED BANK

For brood parasitism by moorhens, see D. W. Gibbons, *Behavioural Ecology and Sociobiology* (1986), 19, 221–232; S. B. McRae, *Journal of Avian Biology* (1996), 27, 311–320, and *Behavioural Ecology* (1998), 9, 93–100. For the bitterling–mussel relationship, see M. Reichard *et al.*, *Evolution* (2010), 64, 3047–3056.

For the synchronous emergence of mayflies as defence to swamp predators, see B. W. Sweeney & R. L. Vannote, *Evolution* (1982), 36, 810–821. For how female water striders have evolved weapons to defend themselves against males, see G. Arnqvist & L. Rowe, *Evolution* (2002), 56, 936–947. For male mimicry by female damselflies as a defence against male harassment, see T. N. Sherratt, *Ecology Letters* (2001), 4, 22–29.

CHAPTER 13. CUCKOOS IN DECLINE

For more on Nicholas Ridley and William Turner, see A. V. Grimstone, *Pembroke College Cambridge: a Celebration* (Pembroke College, 1997). Turner's book on birds is W. Turner, *A Short and Succinct History of the Principal Birds Noticed by Pliny and Aristotle* (1544), edited by A. H. Evans (Cambridge University Press, 1903). For a brilliant history of ornithology from ancient times, including Turner and his contemporaries, see *The Wisdom of Birds* by Tim Birkhead (Bloomsbury, 2008).

The conservation needs of the world's birds are assessed by S. H. M. Butchart *et al.*, in *Handbook of the Birds of the World*, edited by J. del Hoyo, A. Elliott & D. A. Christie, volume 15 (Lynx Edicion, Barcelona, 2010); and costed in D. P. McCarthy *et al.*, *Science* (2012), 338, 946–949.

For a moving account of our spiritual loss from the decline of cuckoos and other summer migrants, see M. McCarthy, *Say Goodbye to the Cuckoo* (John Murray, 2009). The decline of cuckoos in the UK is discussed in D. J. T. Douglas *et al.*, *Oikos* (2010), 119, 1834–1840, and in J. A.Vickery *et al., Ibis* (2014), 156, 1-22. For the rapid recent decline of moths in the UK, see K. F. Conrad *et al.*, *Biological Conservation* (2006), 132, 279–291. Climate change effects on cuckoo migration and host use across Europe are discussed in N. Saino *et al.*, *Biology Letters* (2009), 5, 539–541; A. P. Møller *et al.*, *Proceedings of the Royal Society B* (2011), 278, 733–738. Leonard Jenyns's records of the cuckoo's first arrival in a parish near Wicken Fen are in *A Naturalist's Calendar Kept at Swaffham Bulbeck, Cambridgeshire, by Leonard Blomefield (formerly Jenyns)*, edited by F. Darwin (Cambridge University Press, 1903). For cuckoo first spring arrival dates over the past 50 years at other sites across the UK, see T. H. Sparks *et al.*, *Journal of Ornithology* (2007), 148, 503–511. For observations of cuckoo movements in Africa, see Robert Payne, *The Cuckoos* (Oxford University Press, 2005).

For satellite tracking of cuckoo migration, see the website of the British Trust for Ornithology (www.bto.org).

CHAPTER 14. A CHANGING WORLD

How reed warblers have tracked the cuckoo decline with declining defences over three decades on Wicken Fen is in R. Thorogood & N. B. Davies, *Evolution* (2013), 67, 3545–3555. How reed warbler defences vary between populations in relation to parasitism risk is in A. K. Lindholm, *Journal of Animal Ecology* (1999), 68, 293–309; B. Stokke *et al.*, *Behavioural Ecology* (2008), 19, 612–620; J. A. Welbergen & N. B. Davies, *Behavioural Ecology* (2012), 23, 783–789.

The rapid evolution of blackcap migration is in P. Berthold *et al.*, *Nature* (1992), 360, 668–670; and S. Bearhop *et al.*, *Science* (2005), 310, 502–504. The successful tracking of earlier springs by earlier egg laying of great tits in Wytham Woods is in A. Charmantier *et al.*, *Science* (2008), 320, 800–803. The failure of a long-distance migrant, the pied flycatcher, to track earlier springs is in C. Both & M. E. Visser, *Nature* (2001), 411, 296–298. For more on evolution in response to a changing world, see U. Candolin & B. B. M. Wong, *Behavioural Responses to a Changing World* (Cambridge, 2012).

For the feasts of Henry III, see Oliver Rackham, *The History of the Countryside* (Dent, 1986). The creation of the wonderful RSPB reserve at Lakenheath is described by Norman Sills and Graham Hirons in *British Wildlife* (2011), 22, 381–390. For an optimistic view of how conservation can make a difference, see Andrew Balmford, *Wild Hope: on the Front Lines of Conservation Success* (University of Chicago Press, 2012).

Acknowledgements

I have been so lucky to work in the Zoology Department of Cambridge University, and to have the privilege of a Fellowship of Pembroke College. I could not imagine a happier or more stimulating environment than these two welcoming homes from home. During the last three decades, I have been fortunate to study cuckoos and their hosts with many wonderful colleagues. The ideas discussed in this book have been developed together with them, and it is a pleasure to acknowledge their inspiration and friendship: Michael Brooke, Terry Burke, Stuart Butchart, William Duckworth, Tibor Fuisz, David Gibbons, Lisle Gibbs, Ian Hartley, Alex Kacelnik, Chris Kelly, Rebecca Kilner, Oliver Krüger, Naomi Langmore, Anna Lindholm, Joah Madden, Susan McRae, David Noble, Jarkko Rutila, Michael Sorenson, Claire Spottiswoode, Martin Stevens, Ian Stewart, Cassie Stoddard, Rose Thorogood and Justin Welbergen. I also thank the Natural Environment Research Council and the Royal Society for their generous funding of our studies.

It is a pleasure, too, to thank the National Trust, for giving me the freedom of the nature reserve of Wicken Fen, and the staff there for their encouragement and friendship over many years: Lois Baker, Wilf Barnes, Ian Barton, Tim Bennett, Matthew Chatfield, Joan Childs, Adrian Colston, Howard Cooper, Mark Cornell, Paula Curtis, Anita Escott, John Hughes, Jenny Hupe, Kevin James, Debbie Jones, Jenny Kershaw, Grant Lahore, Carol Laidlaw, Martin Lester, Sandy MacIntosh, Tracey McLean, Ian

Reid, Andy Ross, Ralph Sargeant, Isabel Sedgwick, James Selby, Mike Selby, Chris Soans, Karen Staines, Jack Watson, Jake Williams and Ruby Wood.

The bird ringers of the Wicken Fen Group have generously shared their data on bird populations on the fen. I particularly thank Chris Thorne, who has led this group since 1971, together with Peter Bircham, Phil Harris, Michael Holdsworth, Jo Jones, Neil Larner and Alan Wadsworth.

I'm honoured that James McCallum's drawings grace this book. He is not only a brilliant artist but also an original observer of wildlife, always drawing in the field and spending long hours getting to know the behaviour of his subjects. His drawings are full of light and movement, bringing the dramas of nature straight to the page. They make me smile and long to go out to the fens again, inspired by his artistic eye to have a fresh look at cuckoos and their hosts.

It is a privilege to illustrate the book with Richard Nicoll's award-winning photographs of cuckoos and reed warblers, taken on Wicken Fen. They show that watching these birds is at once both a beautiful and an astonishing experience. I also thank Charles Tyler for his wonderful photographs of cuckoos and meadow pipits, taken on Dartmoor. Claire Spottiswoode has been generous in allowing me to include her photographs, taken in Africa, of egg signatures in hosts and parasites, and of honey-guide chicks with their murderous bill hooks. Others who have generously provided photographs are Bill Carr (courtesy of Alan and Margery Wilkins), Juha Haikola, Dave Leech, Helge Sørensen, Artur Stankiewicz, Keita Tanaka and Ian Wyllie.

Tim Birkhead, Jeremy Mynott and my wonderful editor at Bloomsbury, Bill Swainson, read the whole manuscript and gave excellent advice on an early draft. I also thank Becky Alexander, Anna Simpson and Imogen Corke at Bloomsbury for their expert help at guiding the manuscript through to publication, and Hugh Brazier for superb copy-editing. For help with particular chapters, I thank Joanna Bellis (for cuckoos in medieval poetry), Khadija von Zinnenburg Carroll, Tim Dee, Hildegard Diemberger, Chris Hewson, Rebecca Kilner, David Lahti, Naomi Langmore, Audrey Meaney (for translating the cuckoo riddle in *The Exeter Book* from the Old English), Michael Reeve, Norman Sills, Claire Spottiswoode, Keita Tanaka, Chris Thorne and Rose Thorogood.

My greatest thanks, as always, are to my wife Jan and my daughters Hannah and Alice.

Index

A Note on the Author

Nick Davies is Professor of Behavioural Ecology at the University of Cambridge, and a Fellow of Pembroke College. He is a Fellow of the Royal Society. His cuckoo research has been presented on BBC4 Radio, and as a BBC film, produced by Mike Birkhead and narrated by David Attenborough. His previous books include *Cuckoos, Cowbirds and other Cheats*, which won Best Book of the Year from the British Trust for Ornithology and *British Birds Magazine*.

A Note on the Illustrator

James McCallum is a graduate of The Royal College of Art, best known for his watercolour paintings of the natural world, particularly birds. James was specially commissioned to create the illustrations for this book, observing the cuckoos in Wicken Fen, Cambridgeshire, over three months. He lives in Norfolk.

A Note on the Type

The text of this book is set Adobe Garamond. It is one of several versions of Garamond based on the designs of Claude Garamond. It is thought that Garamond based his font on Bembo, cut in 1495 by Francesco Griffo in collaboration with the Italian printer Aldus Manutius. Garamond types were first used in books printed in Paris around 1532. Many of the present-day versions of this type are based on the *Typi Academiae* of Jean Jannon cut in Sedan in 1615.

Claude Garamond was born in Paris in 1480. He learned how to cut type from his father and by the age of fifteen he was able to fashion steel punches the size of a pica with great precision. At the age of sixty he was commissioned by King Francis I to design a Greek alphabet; for this he was given the honourable title of royal type founder. He died in 1561.